GH00835942

FORMAN'S

Guide To Third Reich German Awards...And Their Values

2ND EDITION

2nd Edition

Copyright 1993
by
Adrian Forman

ISBN No. 912138-52-1

Printed in the United States of America

Designed
by
Roger James Bender

All rights reserved. This book, or parts thereof, may not be reproduced in any form without permission of the author.

Publisher: Adrian Forman (UK distributor only)
608, Duncan House,
Dolphin Square,
London SW1 England

R. James Bender Publishing
P.O. Box 23456, San Jose, Calif. 95153
(408) 225-5777

Introduction

I am pleased to introduce this revised and updated 2nd Edition of Forman's Guide. There are a number of fundamental changes and these I will now outline. The number of illustrations has almost doubled, and this increase reflects more reverse photos of awards as well as variations of manufacture. A major effort has been made to use only original pre-1945 awards, giving an accurate photographic reference for collectors. You will note the references to award documents have been omitted from this text. This important, associated material has also doubled in volume and it has been decided to publish a companion volume later in 1993 on only award documents of the Third Reich; military, political and civil (1933 to 1945). The interest of collectors in this field has increased significantly over recent years and has assumed an importance of its own. This expansion of new material is due to the unselfish generosity of several individuals who have provided numerous photographs and illustrations of awards and their respective documents. I am confident both readers, as well as future collectors and historians will benefit from this. Hopefully, it will also encourage more interest in our hobby.

In addition to the actual awards, this 2nd Edition contains presentation cases, titled paper packets, cartons and the rare outer cartons for cases, which have all recently been increasing in value. Even the more common awards which have remained relatively stable in the past have risen considerably in value. These previously undervalued awards, both historically as well as value wise, include those for acts of heroism and bravery, such as the lower grades of the Iron Cross.

In a specialized field, there are now collectors who are interested in the associate production details of manufacturer's variants and maker's marks. It is understood by collectors and auction houses that values are considerably higher if pieces can be attributed, with documentation, to known political or military leaders, for example, recipients of the Knights Cross.

The discovery of additional historical information since the publication of the 1st Edition in 1988 has required a total re-evaluation of some awards. This is apparent with some of the greater rarities and the more highly valued awards. The true values of such pieces have not always been appreciated if an award was "historically significant", but does not appeal to the collector's market, whereas, a rare award can command a very high price due to collector's desire to own one! The appeal of some pieces affects their values beyond that of their rarity or historical interest, so in the end, you the buyer, can make a "white elephant" of a national treasure, while elevating a medium range award to the level of a "classic", which is usually available from most dealers & auction rooms.

Any realistic catalogue of values is, as its title implies, a guide. Prices are not absolute and the examples tend to be the norm rather than the exception. I hope that this guide will provide information to those who regard themselves as collectors, to those who are interested, or to those who have some relic of World War II in the attic and wonder what it is worth. I wish you good fortune in this respect and enjoyment.

Adrian Forman

Acknowledgments

First, I would like to give a very special thank you to Frau. A. Klietmann of Berlin for allowing me access to the many photographs and information in the Dr. K.G. Klietmann's institute, thus, allowing me to finish a long cherished project. I would also like to thank Frau Teichert, who spent many hours sorting material on my behalf during my visits to Berlin.

Secondly, thank you to my old friend, Lee Bambrough, who not only allowed me access to his library on my many visits, but also encourage me on this and other book projects. A good friend and ex-Berliner, Mr. Gerrard, translated German text and showed me the sights of Berlin as only a Berliner and historian could.

Finally, a thank you to Michelle, my daughter, who spent many hours typing clean text copy for the designer, and real publisher of this book, Roger Bender. Thank you Rog for your professionalism and guidance which makes "Bender Publications" not only unique but the foremost works in their field. They are read and enjoyed by collectors world-wide, who have built up their own Bender library of titles going as far back as 1967.

To those individuals who kindly supplied illustrations of documents, expecting them to be included in this 2nd Edition, I thank you. Your efforts and patience will be rewarded later in 1993 with the companion volume to this 2nd Edition on documents.

My sincere thanks also go to the following:

Ed Anderson (USA)
Lee Bambrough (UK)
Eric Campion (UK)
Christies Auctions - London (UK)
Col. Keith Farnes (UK)
Dr. Beer of Hanseatisches Auktionhaus für Historica (Germany)
V. Bowen (UK)
Roger Hall (USA)
Hanover Photographic Studio (UK)
J. Hanson (USA)
Neil Hardin (USA)
Wolfgang Hermann of Hermann's Historica Auktionhaus (Germany)
Jörg N. Hormann (Germany)
Bob Hritz (USA)
Bob Kraus (USA)
Peter Klubert (Germany)
Edgar Leicher (Germany)
David Littlejohn (UK)
B. Malvaux (France)
Bob McCarthy (USA)
Klaus Peters (Germany)
George Petersen (USA)
Frau Ursula Rudel (Austria)
Andy Southard (USA)
Otto Spronk (Holland)
Joe Stone (USA)
Christian von Tettchinek (Austria)
West Point Museum (USA)
Steve Wolfe (USA)
Ed Zemaitis (USA)

This book is dedicated to the memory of:

Dr. Phil. Kurt-Gerhard Klietmann (1910 - 1990)

Dr. Klietmann, as Director of the Institute for the Scientific Research Study of Orders and Awards, etc, was honoured by the award of the "Bundesverdienst Kreuz" by the then President of the German Bundes Republic, Dr. Weizaecker.

A lifetime's work on many related subjects, made Dr. Klietmann a recognized name associated with many books, publications, and last but not least, a generous sharing of his knowledge with others. The name of Dr. Klietmann will continue, living in the pages and photographs of books, past, present, and future!

I had been requested by Dr. Klietmann's widow Frau A. Klietmann, to advise all concerned, that Dr. Klietmann's Berlin Institute was officially closed at the end of 1990 and that all requests for photographs and information were cancelled as of that date.

The Spanish Civil War 1936~1939

1. Spanish Cross in Gold with Swords & Diamonds
(Spanienkreuz-mit Schwertern in Gold und Brillanten)

(a)	Type A	Award issue silver-gilt & diamonds by Godet of Berlin	$20,000
(b)	Type B	Dress copy in gilt-bronze with imitation stones	10,000
(c)		Deluxe presentation green leather case	*

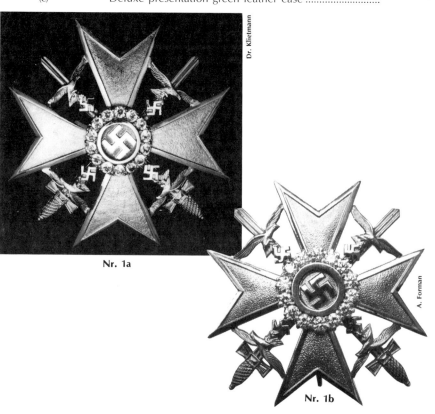

Dr. Klietmann

Nr. 1a

A. Forman

Nr. 1b

2. Spanish Cross in Gold with Swords
(mit Schwertern)

(a)	Type A	Award issue hallmarked "800" or "900". Silver-gilt........	$1,800
(b)	Type B	LDO type in gilt-bronze. Some maker marked	1,000
(c)		Deluxe presentation domed maroon case	400
(d)		LDO type green case...	300

Dr. Klietmann

George Petersen   **Nrs. 2a & 3a**

A. Forman

Nrs. 2a & 3a (Rev.)

A. Forman

Nr. 2c

Adolf Galland wearing the Spanish Cross in Gold with Swords and Diamonds.

7

3. Spanish Cross in Silver with Swords
(mit Schwertern)

(a)	Type A	Award issue hallmarked "800" or "900". Silver. Some maker marked	$1,000
(b)	Type B	LDO type silver-plated. Some maker marked	600
(c)		Deluxe presentation blue case	300
(d)		LDO type green case	200

Nrs. 2b & 3b   Nrs. 2b & 3b (Rev.)

Nrs. 2d, 3d, 4d, 5c, LDO case

4. Spanish Cross in Silver without Swords
(ohne Schwerter)

(a) Type A   Award issue hallmarked "800" or "900". Silver.
               Some maker marked $1,800

(b) Type B   LDO type silver-plated. Some maker marked 850

(c)   Deluxe presentation blue case 300

(d)   LDO type green case 200

Dr. Klietmann

Nr. 4a   **Nr. 4a (Rev.)**

A. Forman

Nr. 4b

5. Spanish Cross in Bronze with Swords
(mit Schwerter)

(a)	Type A	Award issue in bronze. Cut-out swastika detail Some maker marked..	$400
(b)	Type B	LDO type in bronze. Solid swastika & 1st type Luft eagle, Some maker marked..	300
(c)		LDO type green case..	200

Nr. 5a

6. Spanish Cross in Bronze without Swords
(ohne Schwerter)

(a)	Type A	Award issue in bronze. Cut-out swastika detail Some maker marked..	$400
(b)	Type B	LDO type in bronze. Solid swastika & 1st type Luft eagle Some maker marked..	300
(c)		LDO type green case..	200

Nr. 6a

7. Cross of Honour for Relatives of the Dead in Spain (German) (Ehrenkreuz für Hinterbliebene deutscher Spanienkämpfer)

(a) Type A   Award issue in bronze. Olive brown colour...................... $1,500

(b) Type B   Variant. Bronzed silver. (Hallmarked)............................. 1,250

(c)   Presentation blue case.. 500

A. Forman

Nr. 7a

Nr. 7a
(Rev.)

Nr. 7c

George Petersen

8. Tank Badge of the Legion Condor
(Panzertruppen-Abzeichen der Legion Condor)

(a) Type A First issue badge in silver (Portuguese manufacture)........ $2,000

(b) Type B Second issue badge in silvered metal............................... 1,250

(c) *Unique badge in solid gold awarded to Col. von Thoma *

Nr. 8a (Type A)

Nr. 8b (Type B)

Uffz. Erwin Völker shortly before the Berlin victory parade on 6 June 1939.

9. Commemorative Cloth Cuff Title "SPAIN 1936-39"
(Ärmelband "1936 SPANIEN 1939")

(a) Bevo flat silk (maroon) and gold wire,deluxe quality.......................... $1,250

Nr. 9a   Roger Hall

The so-called "Spanish Wound Badge" is catalogued with 1936-45 Wound Badge Section

Orders, Decorations and Medals of the Armed Forces 1939-1945

10. **Grand Cross of the Iron Cross 1939**
    (Eisernes Kreuz - Grosskreuz)

    (a) Type A   Cross awarded to Reichsmarschall Göring. Hallmarked "800"and marked "L/12" (Juncker of Berlin) several specimens exist.. $15,000

    (b) Type B   Crosses manufactured for museum & exhibition displays. Hallmarked "800".. 5,000

    (c)   Deluxe large presentation red leather case. Gold eagle (Wehrmacht) emblem on lid.. 5,000

Dr. Klietmann

Nr. 10a

Nr. 10a (Rev.)

A. Forman

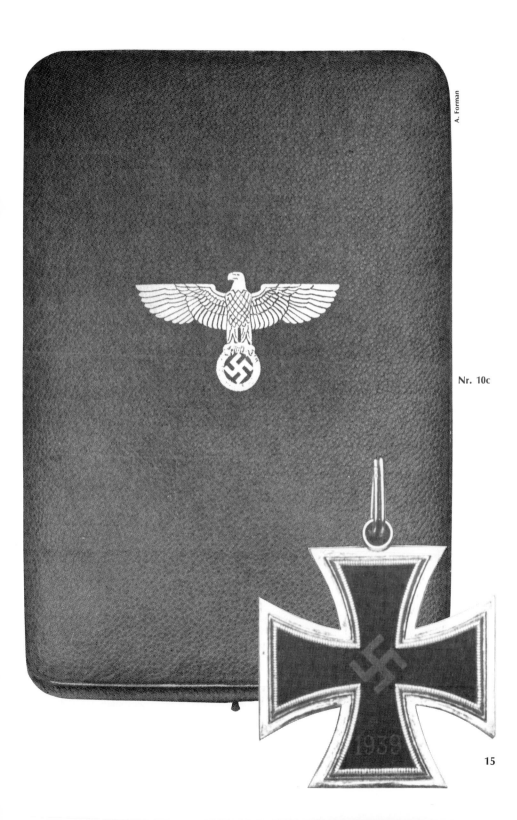

A. Forman

Nr. 10c

15

11. **Knights Cross of the Iron Cross with Golden Oakleaves, Swords & Diamonds**
     (Ritterkreuz des E. K. mit dem Eichenlaub in Gold mit Schwertern und Brillanten)

(a) Type A   Presented by Hitler to Oberst. Hans Rudel.
              In gold with diamonds ....   *
(b) Type B   Dress Copy (Dupla) also presented by Hitler to Rudel.....   *

Nr. 11a, Type A, actual
award worn by Rudel.

12. **Oakleaves Swords & Diamonds to the Knights Cross of the Iron Cross**
     (Eichenlaub mit Schwertern und Brillanten)

1st Pattern.

(a) Type A   Issue Type awarded to Luftwaffe Ace Oberst Mölders
              in 1941. Hallmarked silver with diamonds.......................   *
(b) Type B   Dress Copy in hallmarked silver studded
              with fewer imitation stones.
              Hollow or solid rev. (variants).. $3,000-5,000

2nd Pattern.

(c) Type A   Issue Type in either hallmarked "950 pt" & maker marked
              platinum or gold, "585" studded with diamonds............   *
(d) Type B   Presentation Dress Copy in hallmarked "835" & maker marked
              Silver, studded with diamonds or imitation stones.......... $30,000
(e)   Case...   1,000

L. Bambrough

A. Forman

Nr. 12a, 1st Pattern Brilliants (Oberstlt. Mölders' set).

Nr. 12b, 1st Pattern Brilliants (Dress Copy set, c. 1941).

Nr. 12d, 2nd Pattern, Type B (hallmarked silver), close-up.

S. Wolfe

Dr. Klietmann

Nr. 12c and 12d, 2nd Pattern Brilliants.

Nr. 12e, case for
Nrs. 12a, c, d.

Nr. 12e, case

S. Wolfe

A. Forman

13. Oakleaves and Swords to the Knights Cross of the Iron Cross (Eichenlaub mit Schwertern)

(a) Type A   Issue Type hallmarked "800" silver.
Swords plain reverse $6,500

(b) Type B   Deluxe Type with reverse of swords finely detailed in relief, officially awarded. Examples marked/hallmarked "21 & 900", "L/50 & SILBER 935", "L/13 & 950" "L/12 & 800" 8,500

(c) Type C   Silver-plated - Unmarked. Fine quality striking otherwise it is identical to silver pieces! Examples with reverse of the swords, either detailed or plain 2,500

(d) Case   750

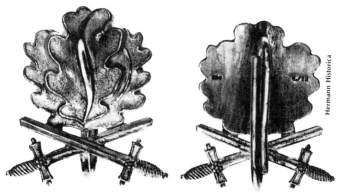

Hermann Historica

Nr. 13b   Nr. 13b (Rev.)

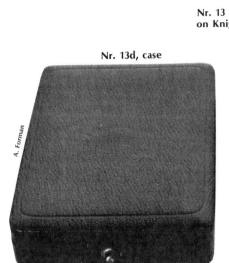

Nr. 13d, case

Nr. 13 as worn
on Knight's Cross.

14. Oakleaves to the Knights Cross of the Iron Cross (Eichenlaub)

(a) Type A   Issue Type in hallmarked "800" silver $3,000

(b) Type B   Deluxe Type also officially awarded. Examples marked-
hallmarked, "21 & 900 L/50" & "SILBER 935",
"L/12 & 800" 4,000

(c) Type C   Silver-plated, unmarked. Fine quality identical to
silver award 2,000

(d)   Case 500

Nr. 14 as worn
on Knight's Cross.

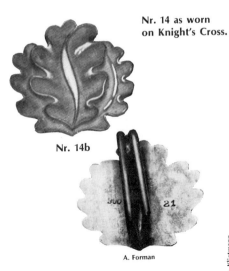

Nr. 14b

A. Forman

19

Nr. 14d, case

A. Forman

15. Knights Cross of the Iron Cross 1939
(Ritterkreuz des Eisernen Kreuzes)

** In 1939, the Führer re-instituted the Iron Cross. The original 1st Form of September 1939 was based on the classic "Schinkel" 1813 form, with smaller swastika and 1939. All classes, except perhaps the Grand Cross, were actually manufactured. These were superseded by the more streamlined 2nd Form pieces later in 1939.

*** In October 1939, after the successful Polish campaign, the Führer awarded the newly instituted Knight's Cross to members of the German High Command at a victory ceremony.

The presentation cases would have contained one of two combinations of awards, depending on the officer's previous war service in relation to the newly constituted Iron Cross regulations of 1939. They were as follows:

(i)   Cased set: Knights Cross with Iron Cross, 1st and 2nd Class 1939.

(ii)   Cased Knights Cross and matching cased set of 1st and 2nd Class Bars to the Iron Cross 1939.

(iii)   1939 Large Deluxe Red Leather Presentation Cased Sets, as above ....   *

1st Form (Erste Form)[1]

(a)   Design consisted of "Schinkel" form, cross with a unique "loop", rather than "eye" (Öse) suspender-ring. Nickel frame and a non-iron center..   *

---

[1]The 1st form (Erste Form) Iron Cross series of September 1939 (See - Reichsgesetzblatt, Jahrgang 1939, Teil 1 - 1575/1576,) was awarded in small quantities from several manufacturers from existing stocks in 1939-40 and perhaps as late as 1941 with the introduction of the new official LDO Regulations, dated March 1, 1941. The pieces, including the 1939 Bars (Spange,) were of nickel (Neu-Silber) with non-iron centers based on specimens examined by the author.

A. Forman

Nr. 15 (i), 1939 large deluxe
red leather presentation
case.

A. Forman

Nr. 15 (ii), 1939 cased bars
to Iron Cross set.

21

Hitler presents Generaloberst von Brauchitsch with the red leather case containing the 1939 Knight's Cross set.

Dr. Klietmann

Nr. 15, 1st Form

Oberleutnant Dietrich Steinhardt, who was awarded his Knight's Cross on October 24, 1939, appears to be wearing the 1st Form.

2nd Form (Zweite Form)

(b) Type A   Official issue Type hallmarked "800"
silver. Iron center... $2,000 -2,500

(c) Type B   Deluxe Type also officially awarded. Examples marked-
hallmarked, "L/12 & 800", "2 & 800", "4 & 935",
"20 & 800", also KC hallmarked, "800" & "65"
on suspender-loop.. 3,000

(d) Type C   Official Type - Unmarked silver or silver-plated,examples
known, non-iron centers. Unmarked & marked examples of
suspender-loops known.
Such types have been awarded $1,500-2,000

(e)   Case.. 400

(f)   Titled outer carton for case. With makers address........... *

A. Forman

Nr. 15c

A. Forman

Nr. 15e

Nr. 15e

Nr. 15f

16. Iron Cross 1st Class 1939
(Eisernes Kreuz 1. Klasse)

1st Form (Erste Form).

(a)   Design consisted of a smaller, stylized "Schinkel" form cross, with small swastika & 1939 .... $350

2nd Form (Zweite Form).

(b) Type A   Early quality award or screwback type............................... $90-120

(c) Type B   Late war type 70

Nr. 16a "Schinkel"

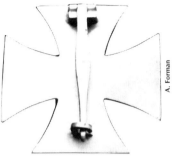

Nr. 16b, Type A

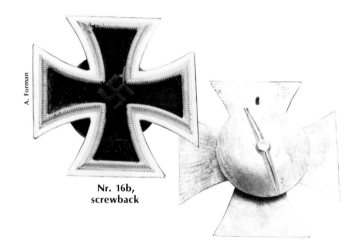

**Nr. 16b,
screwback**

(d)	Type C	Field service - Cloth type sewn to jacket. Usually black velvet or felt with white/silver detail in relief	250-400
(e)		Cases. (Pinback or screwback)	35-50
(f)		Titled outer carton for case. Usually with maker's address	40-50

Nr. 16d, Type C

Nr. 16e

Nr. 16f

17. Bar to the Iron Cross 1st Class 1939
(Spange 1939 zum EK. 1. KLASSE 1914)

1st Form (Erste Form).

(a) Design consisted of eagle and swastika on "1939" bar
     with "scalloped" ends, rather than the later
     "angled" design.. *

(b) Case. 1st Form Bar to Iron Cross 1st Class 1939,
     in silver, on lid .... *

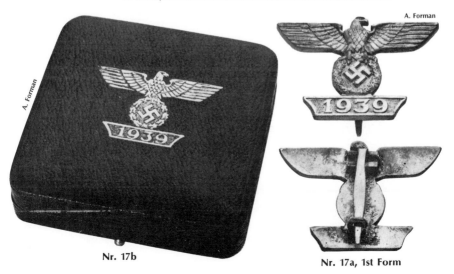

Nr. 17b

Nr. 17a, 1st Form

27

Feldmarschall von Rundstedt wears Nr. 17a, 1st Form (note scalloped ends).

General der Panzertruppen Guderian also wears Nr. 17a, 1st Form, as well as Nr. 19a, 1st Form.

2nd Form (Zweite Form).

(c)	Type A	Early quality award, silver-plated. Some maker marked. Flat tapered or needle pin	$120
(d)	Type B	Late war type, silvered zinc	75
(e)	Type C	Screwback type	175
(f)	Type D	Deluxe Dual - 1914 Iron Cross and Bar to Iron Cross 1939 combined. Maker marked. Pinback or screwback	500
(g)		Cases. (Pinback or screwback)	50-100
(h)		Titled Outer Carton for Case	40-60

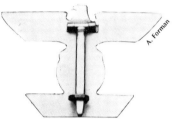

Nr. 17c, Type A

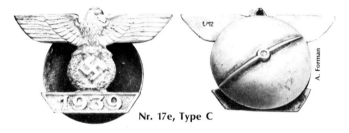

Nr. 17e, Type C

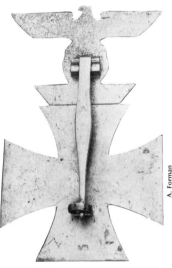

Nr. 17f, Type D

30

A. Forman

C. v. Tettinck

Nr. 17f, screwback

Nr. 17g

A. Forman

Spange zum Eisernen Kreuz 1. Klasse

Nur vom Beliehenen zu öffnen

Nr. 17h

18.   Iron Cross 2nd class 1939
(Eisernes Kreuz II Klasse)

1st Form (Erste Form).

(a)   Design consisted of a smaller, stylized "Schinkel"
                  form Cross, with small swastika and 1939.......................... $150

Nr. 18a, 1st Form

2nd Form (Zweite Form).

(b) Type A   Early quality award.. 50
(c) Type B   Late war type 30
(d)   Titler paper packet or LDO case.. 30-50

Nr. 18b, Type A

A. Forman

A. Forman

Eisernes Kreuz
2. Klasse
1939

Eisernes Kreuz
2. Klasse

A. Forman

E. Anderson

Eisernes Kreuz
2. Klasse
1939

Nr. 18d variants

Nr. 18d LDO case

19. Bar to the Iron Cross, 2nd Class 1939
(Spange 1939 zum E. K. II Klasse 1914)

1st Form (Erste Form).

(a) Design consisted of eagle and swastiska set on
"1939" bar with "scalloped" ends, rather than
the later "angled" design.. *

A. Forman

Nr. 19a, 1st Form

2nd Form (Zweite Form).

(b)	Type A	Early quality award, silver-plated...	$75
(c)	Type B	Late war type. Silvered zinc..	50
(d)	Type C	"25mm" reduction, quality silver-plated...........................	100
(e)		Titled paper packet	40-50
(f)		LDO slip case	50

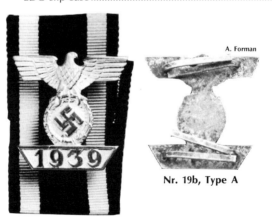

A. Forman

Nr. 19b, Type A

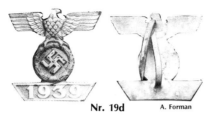

Nr. 19d

A. Forman

A. Forman

Nr. 19e

Nr. 19f

Spange zum

Eisernen Kreuz II. Klasse

A. Forman

A. Forman

Spange
zum
Eisernen Kreuz
2. Klasse
1939

E. Anderson

Nr. 19e

35

20. Roll of Honour Clasp for the Army 1941
(Ehrenblattspange-Heer)

(a)	Awarded to recipient mounted on Iron Cross ribbon	$1,000
(b)	Case	200

21. Roll of Honour Clasp for the Navy 1943
(Ehrentafelspange-Kriegsmarine)

(a)	Awarded to recipient mounted on Iron Cross ribbon	$2,000
(b)	Case	200

*Only 26 actual awards by Grand Admiral Dönitz in 1944-45, making actual documented awards excessively rare, most mint and unissued!

22. Roll of Honour Clasp for the Luftwaffe
(Ehrentafelspange-Luftwaffe)

(a)	Awarded to recipient mounted on Iron Cross ribbon	$1,300
(b)	Case	200

A. Forman

Nr. 20a   Nr. 21a   Nr. 22a

A. Forman

A. Forman

Nr. 20b

Nr. 21b   A. Forman

Nr. 22b   A. Forman

A. Forman

Nrs. 20b, 21b, 22b

23. The Commendation Certificates of the High Command & Führer 1941-45
(Anerkennungsurkunde der Oberbefehlshabers des Heeres und Führer)

(a) Type A   1st issue Certificate of the Army High Command, signed by von Brauchitsch 1941, (A5) $2,500

(b) Type B   2nd issue Certificate of the Führer. Signed by A. Hitler. (Facsimile), 1942-1945 (A4) 1, 800

Nr. 23a

Nr. 23b

L. Bambrough

24. German Cross in Gold 1941
(Deutsches Kreuz)

(a)   Type A   Metal & enamel, 4, 5, 6, 8, or 10 rivets
                          Some maker marked $700-800

(b)   Type B   Bullion & cloth field service issue.
                          (Army-Navy-Luftwaffe)... 150-250

(c)   Large case for Type A. (gold border line to lid)................ 150

(see note on next page)

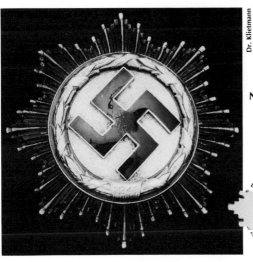

Dr. Klietmann

Nr. 24a

A. Forman

Note: Type A awards had lead-ball type multiple rivet construction and were very heavy, followed later by domed rivet, heavy type. First awards were by Deschler of Munich. Final lightweight, cupronickel types were of 4-rivet construction.

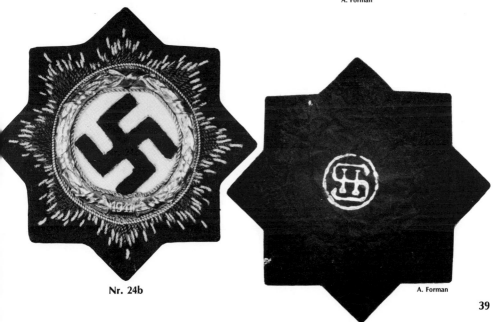

Nr. 24b   A. Forman

Col. K. Farnes

Note the 10-rivet construction of this German Cross
in Gold. It is purportedly the first such decoration
awarded.

Preparing for a field award ceremony.

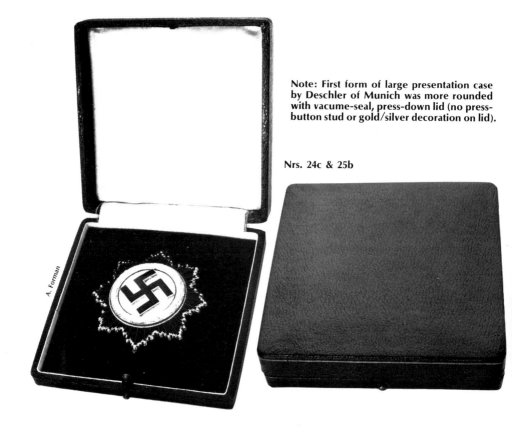

Note: First form of large presentation case by Deschler of Munich was more rounded with vacume-seal, press-down lid (no press-button stud or gold/silver decoration on lid).

Nrs. 24c & 25b

A. Forman

25. German Cross in Silver 1941 (Deutsches Kreuzes)

   (a) Type A   Metal & enamel, 4, 5, 6, 8, or 10 rivets...................... $1,000-1,200
                           Some with makers marks
   (b)   Large case for Type. A. (silver border line to lid).............. 200

(see note above)

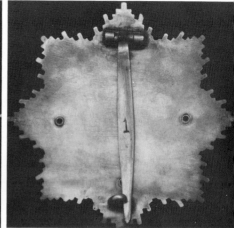

                                    Nr. 25a   Dr. Klietmann

26. Special Grade of the German Cross in Gold with Diamonds (Deutsches Kreuzes in Gold mit Brillanten)

** Approximately 20 specimens were manufactured by Rath of Munich in silver with Diamonds.

(a)   German Cross in Gold with Diamonds............................. $25,000

(b)   Deluxe presentation red case... 5,000

Nr. 26a

Dr. Klietmann

S. Wolfe

S. Wolfe

Nr. 26b

27. Knights Cross of the War Merit Cross in Gold with Swords 1944 (Goldenes Ritterkreuz des KVK mit Schwertern)

    (a)   Fine quality gold-plated silver. Unmarked. A few examples are known with "900" and maker-marked "1"............ 7,000

    (b)   Large blue case.. 600

Nr. 27   Dr. Klietmann

Nr. 28   Dr. Klietmann

28. Knights Cross of the War Merit Cross in Gold without Swords 1944
(Goldenes Ritterkreuz des KVK ohne Schwerter)

(a)   Fine quality gold-plated silver. Unmarked. A few examples
are known with "900" and maker-marked "1"............ $6,000

(b)   Large blue case... 600

Case for Nrs. 27, 28, 29 & 30.

29. Knights Cross of the War Merit Cross with Swords 1940 (Ritterkreuz des KVK mit Schwertern)

(a)	Type A	Early issue type, quality hallmarked "900" silver and usually with maker's mark, "1 "	$4,000
(b)	Type B	Late war issue, silver-plated. Unmarked	1,500
(c)		Large blue case	400

Nr. 29a

Dr. Klietmann

30. Knights Cross of the War Merit Cross without Swords 1940 (Ritterkreuz des KVK ohne Schwerter)

(a) Type A   Early issue type, quality hallmarked "900" silver
and usually with maker's mark, "1 "................................ $3,500

(b) Type B   Late war issue silver-plated. Unmarked............................ 1, 500

(c)   Large blue case.. 400

Nr. 30a

Dr. Klietmann

31. War Merit Cross 1st Class with Swords 1939 (Kriegsverdienstkreuz mit Schwertern)

(a)	Type A	Early issue, quality silver-plated..	$75
(b)	Type B	Late war issue, silvered zinc...	50
(c)	Type C	Screwback type	90
(d)		Case. (pinback & screwback types)....................................	30-50
(e)		Titled outer carton, maker marked....................................	50

Dr. Klietmann

Nr. 31a

A. Forman

Nr. 31c

A. Forman

A. Forman

Nr. 31d

Nr. 31e

KRIEGS-
VERDIENSTKREUZ
1. KLASSE
MIT SCHWERTERN

A. Forman

32. War Merit Cross 1st Class without Swords 1939
(Kriegsverdienstkreuz ohne Schwerter)

(a)	Type A	Early issue, quality silver-plated	$60
(b)	Type B	Late war issue, silvered zinc	40
(c)	Type C	Screwback type	90
(d)		Case (pinback & screwback types)	30-50
(e)		Titled outer carton, maker marked	50

Dr. Klietmann

A. Forman

A. Forman

Nr. 32a

Nr. 32c

A. Forman

Nr. 32d

A. Forman

Nr. 32e

KRIEGS-
VERDIENSTKREUZ
1. KLASSE

33. War Merit Cross 2nd Class with Swords 1939
(Kriegsverdienstkreuz II mit Schwertern)

(a)	Type A	Early issue type in bronze.............................	$20-25
(b)	Type B	Late war issue bronzed zinc	15
(c)		Titled paper packet, maker marked..............................	15
(d)		LDO case	40

Dr. Klietmann

A. Forman

A. Forman

Nr. 33a

Kriegs-
Verdienſtkreuz
2. Klaſſe
mit Schwertern

Kriegs-
Verdienſtkreuz
2. Klaſſe
mit Schwertern

Upper Right: Nr. 33c,
small packet.
Right: Nr. 33c,
large packet

A. Forman

34. War Merit Cross, 2nd Class without Swords 1939 (Kriegsverdienst II ohne Schwerter)

(a)	Type A	Early issue type in bronze	$15-20
(b)	Type B	Late war issue bronzed zinc	12
(c)		Titled paper packet, maker marked	12
(d)		LDO case	40

Nr. 34a

Upper left: Nr. 34c, small packet.
Left: Nr. 34c, large packet.

51

A. Forman

Nrs. 33d & 34d

A. Forman

35. War Merit Medal 1939
(Kriegsverdienstmedaille)

(a)   Struck in bronze.. $15-20

(b)   Titled paper packet, maker marked................................ 15

Dr. Klietmann

Nr. 35a

Nr. 35b

A. Forman

36. War Commemorative Medal 1939-1940
(Medaille zur Erinnerung an den Krieg 1939/1940)

   (a)   Type A   Struck in bronze. (Combatants)..   *

   (b)   Type B   Struck in iron.(Non-Combatants)..................................... $1,500

              **Not awarded.

Nr. 36b

Dr. Klietmann

Reverse for
Nrs. 36 & 37

37. War Commemorative medal 1939-1941
(Medaille zur Erinnerung an den Krieg 1939/1941)

   (a)   Type A   Struck in bronze. (Combatants)..   *

   (b)   Type B   Struck in iron. (Non-Combatants)...................................   *

              **Not awarded

38. Commemorative Medal of 13 March 1938
(Medaille zur Erinnerung an den 13 März 1938)

   (a)   Known as"Entry into Austria"medal,

                 Silver-plated bronze.. $40

   (b)   Red case   30

Dr. Klietmann

Nr. 38a

A. Forman

Nr. 38b

39. Commemorative Medal of 1 October 1938
(Medaille zur Erinnerung an den 1 Oktober 1938)

(a)	Known as, "Entry into Sudentenland" medal in bronze	$30
(b)	Brown case...	25
(c)	LDO titled paper packet...	20

Dr. Klietmann

Nr. 39a

Nr. 39c

Nr. 39b

A. Forman

40. Prague Castle bar for Commemorative Medal of 1 October 1938 (Spange, "Pragerburg")

(a)	Struck in bronze, some with makers mark	$60
(b)	LDO slip case or titled paper packet	25-50

Nr. 40a

Nr. 40b

41. Commemorative Medal of the Return of the Memel District 1939 (Medaille zur Erinnerung an die Heimkehr des Memellandes)

(a)	Type A	Early issue struck in bronze	$150
(b)	Type B	Later issue in bronzed zinc	120
(c)		Red case	30

Nr. 41a

42. West Wall Medal 1939
(Deutsches Schutzwall-Ehrenzeichen)

(a)	Type A	Early issue struck in bronze	$20-25
(b)	Type B	Later issue in bronzed zinc or alloy	18
(c)		Bronze Award Clasp "1944" (Not awarded)....................	*
(d)		Titled paper packet	15
(e)		Deluxe presentation case	*

Dr. Klietmann

Nr. 42

A. Forman

Nr. 42d

43. The Italo-German Campaign Medal in Africa 1941
(Medaille für den Italiensch-Deutschen Feldzug in Afrika)

(a)	Type A	Early issue struck in bronze with makers mark......	$75
(b)	Type B	Later issue in silvered or grey metal................	50
(c)		Titled cellophane packet. Italian maker	50

Nr. 43

44. Medal for the Winter Campaign in Russia 1941-1942
("Winterschlacht im Osten 1941-1942")

(a)	Type A	Early issue, with makers mark	$30
(b)	Type B	Later issue in silvered/grey zinc	20
(c)		Titled paper packet, maker marked	20

Nr. 44

Nr. 44c

45. Bravery and Commemorative Medal of the Spanish"Blue Division"1941
(Tapferkeits-und Erinnerungsmedaille der Spanischen"Blauen Division)

(a) Type A   German manufactur bronzed zinc with maker's mark ... $75
(b) Type B   Spanish manufacture. Bronzed metal. Poor quality........   40
(c)   Titled paper packet   50

Nr. 45a

D. Littlejohn

Nr. 45b

46. **Spanish Decoration to Commemorate the Spanish "Blue Division on the Russian Front 1941.**

    (a) Type A   Fine quality silver-plated & enameled
                         German manufacture $175
    (b) Type B   Spanish manufacture, poorer quality and finish 100

Dr. Klietmann

Nr. 46b

60

47. **Ostvolk Decorations for Bravery or Merit on the Eastern Front 1942**

(Tapferkeits-und Verdienst-Auszeichnung für Angehörige der Ostvölker)

(a)	1st Class in Gold with Swords	$100
(b)	2nd Class in Gold with Swords	65
(c)	1st Class in Gold	85
(d)	2nd Class in Gold	55
(e)	1st Class in Silver with Swords	65
(f)	2nd Class in Silver with Swords	55
(g)	1st Class in Silver	60
(h)	2nd Class in Silver	55
(i)	2nd Class in Bronze with Swords	55
(j)	2nd Class in Bronze	50
(k)	Black case for 1st Class awards	50
(l)	Titled paper packets for 2nd Class awards	50

Dr. Klietmann

A. Forman

Nrs. 47a & 47e

Reverse, Nrs. 47a, c, e & g.

Nrs. 47c and 47g

Nrs. 47c & g cased.

A. Forman

A. Forman

Nrs. 47b, 47f & 47i

Nrs. 47b, 47d, 47f,
47h & 47J.

Dr. Klietmann

Nrs. 47d, 47h & 47j.

Nr. 47k for 1st Class
in Silver with Swords.

Nr. 47k for 1st Class in
Silver without Swords.

A. Forman

Nr. 47l, titled
packet for 47d.

A. Forman

Verdienst-
Auszeichnung
für
Angehörige der Ostvölker

2. Klasse in Gold

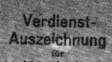

Verdienst-
Auszeichnung
für
Angehörige der Ostvölker

1. Klasse in Silber

Nr. 47l, titled
packet for 47g.

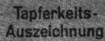

Tapferkeits-
Auszeichnung
für
Angehörige der Ostvölker

2. Klasse in Silber

Nr. 47l, titled
packet for 47h.

63

Nr. 47l, titled
packet for 47i.

Nr. 47l, titled
packet for 47j.

A. Forman

48. **The Young Cossack Officers School Badge c. 1941.**
(Jung-Kosaken-Abzeichen)

Silver-plated alloy (lightweight). Reverse; hollow pinback.
Thin needle pin or two loops.. $1,000

Dr. Klietmann

Nr. 48

A. Forman

49. 5th Don Cossacks Cavalry Regiment Cross 1941 (5. Don Kosakenreiter-Rgt. Kreuz)

Aluminium, matt painted. Reverse; press-moulded pin fittings.
(Mold shows in relief on front below "5"). Steel safety-pin $1,000

Nr. 49

50. Cossacks Cross of the 2nd Siberian Cavalry Regiment (Kosakenkreuz des Siber-Reiter-Rgt. Nr. 2)

Original issue enamel and gilt bronze by
(Croat) Knaub of Zagreb. Pinback $1,500

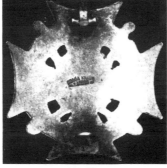

Nr. 50

51. The P. O. A. (ROA) Vlassov Officers School Badge c. 1941
(1. Offizier-Schule der ROA Traditionsabzeichen)

**Original issue in grey zinc with matt painted center.
Pinback. Serial numbered on reverse.. $2,000

Nr. 51

Nr. 52

52. The Narvik Campaign Shield 1940
   (Narvikschild)

(a)	Type A	Silver grey zinc as issued to the Army, Luftwaffe and Waffen SS..	$75-85
(b)	Type B	Matt gilt zinc as issued to the Navy....................................	110
(c)		Cloth backing for either Luftwaffe, Army or W-SS...........	100-150
(d)		Cloth backing for Navy issue gilt shield.............................	175

53. The Cholm Campaign Shield 1942
   (Cholmschild)

(a)	Type A	Pressed-metal shield with no backing cloth	$400
(b)	Type B	Pressed-metal shield with cloth backing for Army, W-SS or Luftwaffe..	600
(c)	Type C	Zinc variant with cloth backing for Luftwaffe, Army or W-SS	500

Dr. Klietmann

Nr. 53b

Nr. 53c

A. Forman

54. The Crimea Campaign Shield 1941-1942
(Krimschild)

(a)	Type A	Early issue in pressed bronzed tin (convex)........................	$50
(b)	Type B	Later type in bronzed alloy or zinc	40
(c)		Shield with cloth backing for Luftwaffe............................	100
(d)		Shield with cloth backing for Navy	125
(e)		Shield with cloth backing for Army or Waffen-SS	80

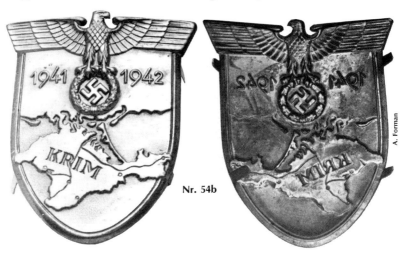

Nr. 54b

A. Forman

Dr. Klietmann

Nr. 54e

55. Demjansk Shield 1943
(Demjanskschild)

(a) Type A   Pressed-metal shield without any cloth backing.............. $110

(b) Type B   Shield with cloth backing for Army/W-SS........................   150

Nr. 55a

Dr. Klietmann

Nr. 55b

56. The Kuban Campaign Shield 1943 (Kubanschild)

(a) Type A   Early issue in pressed bronzed tin (convex) $70

(b) Type B   Later type in bronzed alloy or zinc 60

(c)   Shield with cloth backing for Luftwaffe............................ 120

(d)   Shield with cloth backing for Navy 135

(e)   Shield with cloth backing for Army/W-SS 90

Nr. 56d

A. Forman

57. Warsaw Shield 1944
(Warschauschild)

**No shields produced, only a few manufacuturer's
sample matrices exist.. *

Dr. Klietmann

Nr. 57

58. Lorient Shield 1944
(Lorientschild)

**Arm shield in form of identification plaque stamped
"Festung Lorient". Converted from basic army I.D. disc and sewn
to arm of tunic.. *

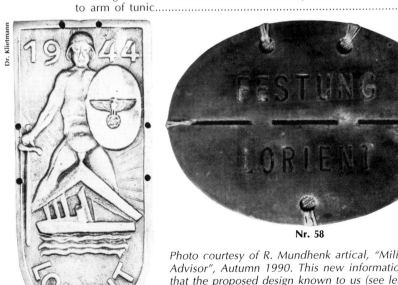

Dr. Klietmann

Nr. 58

*Photo courtesy of R. Mundhenk artical, "Military
Advisor", Autumn 1990. This new information shows
that the proposed design known to us (see left) was, in
fact, not issued.*

71

59. The Lapland Campaign Shield 1945
(Lapplandschild)

**Variations exist in crude aluminium, zinc or brass materials $350

Nr. 59

60. "Crete" Commemorative Cuff Title 1942
(Ärmelband "Kreta")

(a) Type A   Superior quality manufacture with 9-leaf cone $275
(b) Type B   Normal issue with 7-leaf cone 225

Nr. 60b

61. "Africa" Commemorative Cuff Title 1941
(Armelband "Afrika")

Cloth cuff title $175

Nr. 61

62. "Metz 1944" Cuff Title
(Ärmelband Metz 1944)

**Institutued by Hitler, and manufactured, but few awarded.

(a)	Type A	Embroidered silk variant..	$400
(b)	Type B	Embroidered silver wire variant...	500

Hritz

Nr. 62a

63. "Courland" Campaign Cuff Title 1944
(Ärmelband "Kurland)

(a)	Type A	Superior quality wide bevo-style silk cotton	$550
(b)	Type B	Cruder variations in cotton etc..	350

Dr. Klietmann

Nr. 63a

64. Army/Waffen-SS Infantry Assault Badge 1939
(Infanterie-Sturmabzeichen)

(a)	Type A	Early quality silver-plated badge...	$40-50
(b)	Type B	Later issues in silvered/grey alloy or zinc............................	30
(c)		Titled paper packet or cardboard carton.........................	20-50

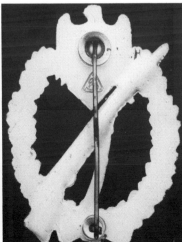

Dr. Klietmann

Nr. 64a

65. Army/Waffen-SS Infantry Assault Badge Bronze Grade 1940 (Infanterie-Sturmabzeichen)

(a)	Type A	Early quality bronze..	$50-60
(b)	Type B	Later issues in bronzed alloy or zinc..................................	45
(c)		Titled paper packet or cardboard carton.........................	25-50

Nr. 65b

66. Army/Waffen-SS Tank Battle Badge in Silver 1940 (Panzerkampfabzeichen in Silber)

(a)	Type A	Early quality silver-plated badge..	$50-60
(b)	Type B	Later issues in silvered/grey alloy or zinc............................	45
(c)		Titled paper packet or cardboard carton.........................	25-50

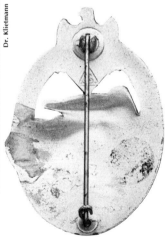

Nr. 66a

67. Army/Waffen-SS Tank Battle Badge in Bronze 1940 (Panzerkampfabzeichen in Bronze)

(a)	Type A	Early quality bronze..	$60-70
(b)	Type B	Later issues in bronzed alloy or zinc.................................	50
(c)		Titled paper packet or cardboard carton.........................	25-50

Nr. 67a

68. Army/Waffen-SS Special Grade of the Tank Battle Badge in Silver (Panzerkampfabzeichen in Silber mit der Einsatzzahl)

(a)	Type A	Heavy silver-plated, rivetted issue by "JFS" or unmarked	
(b)	Type B	Medium weight silvered, rivetted issue by "GB" or unmarked	
(c)		Grade II for 25 Engagements................................	$400-500
(d)		Grade III for 50 Engagements...............................	600-700
(e)		Grade IV for 75 Engagements..............................	1,800
(f)		Grade V for 100 Engagements............................	2,500

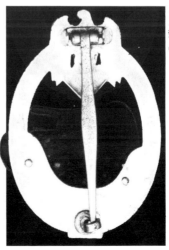

Nr. 68c,
Type B

Dr. Klietmann

Nr. 68d

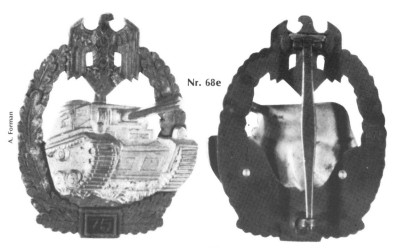

A. Forman

Nr. 68e

Nr. 68f

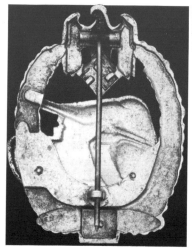

Dr. Klietmann

69. **Army/Waffen-SS Special Grade of the Tank Battle Badge in Bronze**
(Panzerkampfabzeichen in Bronze mit der Einsatzzahl)

(a) Type A   Heavy quality olive-bronze rivetted issue
                   by "JFS" or unmarked.
(b) Type B   Medium weight rivetted issue by "GB" or unmarked
(c)   Grade II for 25 Engagements $500-600
(d)   Grade III for 50 Engagements 800-950
(e)   Grade IV for 75 Engagements 2,000
(f)   Grade V for 100 Engagements 2,200-2,500

Nr. 69c

A. Forman

77

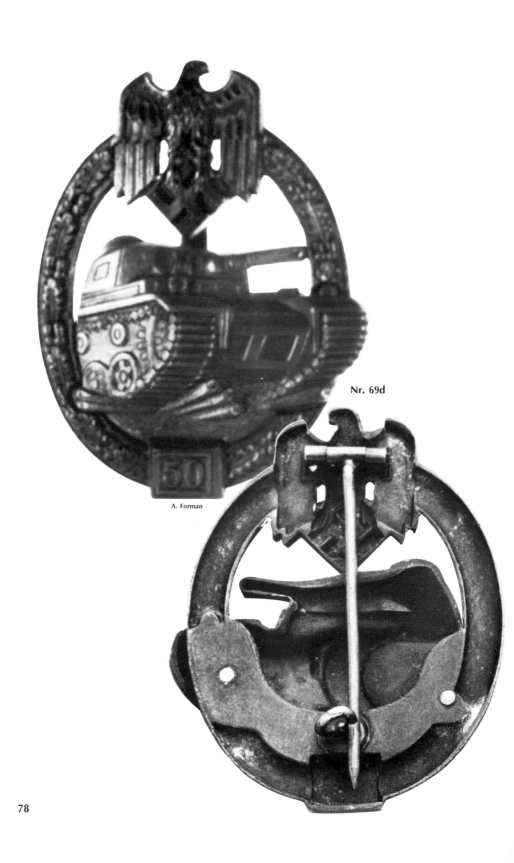

Nr. 69d

A. Forman

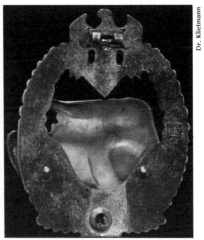

Dr. Klietmann

Nr. 69e

A. Forman

Nr. 69f

70. Army/Waffen-SS General Assault Badge 1940 (Allgemeines-Sturmabzeichen)

(a)	Type A	Early silver-plated issue	$50-60
(b)	Type B	Later issues in silvered/grey alloy or zinc	40
(c)		Titled paper packet or cardboard carton	25-50

Nr. 70

71. Army/Waffen-SS Special Grade of the General Assault Badge 1943
(Allgemeines Sturmabzeichen mit der Einsatzzahl)

(a) Type A   Heavy silver-plated, rivetted issue by "JFS" or unmarked
(b) Type B   Medium weight silvered, rivetted issue by "GB" or unmarked
(c)   Grade II for 25 Engagements $400-500
(d)   Grade III for 50 Engagements 600-700
(e)   Grade IV for 75 Engagements 1, 800
(f)   Grade V for 100 Engagements 2, 500

Nr. 71c

Dr. Klietmann

Nr. 71d

Dr. Klietmann

Nr. 71e

Dr. Klietmann

Nr. 71f

72. Army Flak Badge 1941
(Heeres-Flakabzeichen)

(a)	Type A	Heavy quality oxidised, silver-plated issue, some with makers mark	$300
(b)	Type B	Later issue in silvered/grey zinc or alloy, some with makers mark	250
(c)		Titled paper packet or cardboard carton	75-100

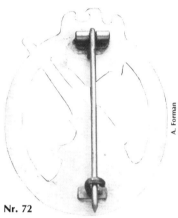

Nr. 72

73. Army/Waffen-SS Close Combat Clasp 1942-45
(Nahkampfspange)

(a)	Type A	Heavy early plated tombak with maker's mark	
(b)	Type B	Heavy or medium weight with gilt, silver or bronze, grey zinc or alloy	
(c)	Type C	Deluxe quality tombak gold-plated, rivetted. Type presented by the Führer or Reichsführer-SS, 1944-45	
(d)		Grade I Bronze for 15 Combat Days	$100-150

Nr. 73

Nr. 73g

(e)	Grade II Silver for 30 Combat Days....................................	250-300
(f)	Grade III Gold for 50 Combat Days....................................	750
(g)	Special presentation, deluxe rivetted	
	Grade III Gold Clasp	4,000
(h)	Black case for deluxe presentation	
	Grade III Gold Clasp..	750

Titled box for Nr. 73d.

Nr. 73g
cased

A. Forman

Nr. 73h

Hitler personally awards the Close Combat Clasp in Gold at the Führerhauptquartier at Rasten-
burg.

74. Army Parachutists Badge 1937-45
(Fallschirmschützen-Abzeichen des Heeres)

(a)	Type A	Deluxe presentation, hallmarked, "800 " silver & inscribed	$2,000
(b)	Type B	Deluxe quality, lightweight aluminum. Unmarked or by C.E. Juncker.........	1,000
(c)	Type C	Quality fine zinc, later war issue..........	700
(d)	Type D	Other ranks type in machine-embroidered (late war)cotton	600
(e)		Deluxe case for presentation, hallmarked silver badge............	400

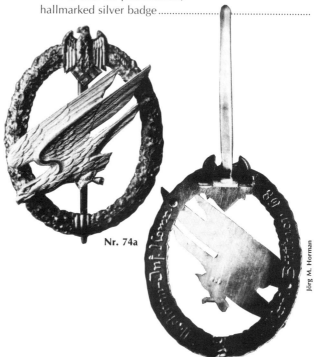

Nr. 74a

Jörg M. Horman

Nr. 74b

Dr. Klietmann

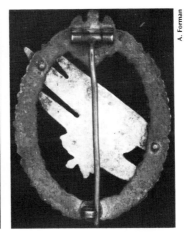

Nr. 74c

Nr. 74d

Oberlt. Alfred Schwarzmann wears the Army Parachutist Badge.

75. Anti-Partisan War Badge 1944-45
(Bandenkampfabzeichen/1944-45)

(a) Type A — First issue manufactured by "Juncker" with stylised skull, cut-out serpents. Reverse either semi-hollow or solid. Struck in tombak & either alloy or zinc. Either flat or needle pin

(b) Type B — Later issue of another manufacturer, with small skull, massive heavy solid badge. Reverse solid & flat. In alloy or zinc

(c) Type C — Deluxe Special Grade III Gold Badge, presented by Reichsführer-SS in 1945. Gold-plated tombak

(d) Grade I Bronze for 20 Combat Days $500

(e) Grade II Silver for 50 Combat Days 900

(f) Grade III Gold for 150 Combat Days 1,200

(g) Deluxe Special Grade III presentation badge .... *

(h) Blue case for Grade III Gold Badge 400

(i) Blue case for deluxe Special Grade III presentation badge . *

*In fact, only four Deluxe Special Grade III presentation badges were personally awarded by Reichsführer-SS Himmler at his headquarters on 15th February 1945. These badges were specially made & hand finished by "C.E. Juncker" of Berlin. Deluxe quality convex gold-plated tombak with blued-steel finish blade & finely detailed cut-out serpents. Wide silver pin on reverse. Most collections have examples of the Grade III Gold Badge non-presentation Type A. To date, the only known example of the 4 Presentation Badges is that illustrated in Benders Littlejohn & Dodkins VOL. II & described in Dr. K.G. KLIETMANN'S book, "Deutsche Auszeichnung" Vol. II (1970 - Adrian Forman Collection). It should be noted that this important & unique historical information, now repeated in several books, should be credited to Dr. Klietmann, as researched & given to Adrian Forman in 1970 (Includes Berlin Newspaper-VB details of Himmler presentations in1945, Ex Dr. Klietmanns Archive).

Dr. Klietmann

Nr. 75a, Type A

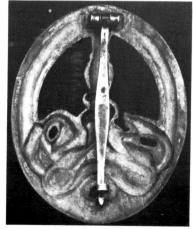

Nr. 75a, reverse

Nr. 75b, Type B

Nr. 75g, Type C

76. Special Grade of the Anti-Partisan War Badge in Gold with Diamonds 1944-45
(Bandenkampfabzeichen mit Brillanten)

**Twenty examples in silver-gilt with diamonds were
manufactured but not awarded.. *

77. Army Balloon Observers Badge 1944
(Ballonbeobachterabzeichen des Heeres)

(a)	Grade I Bronze for 20 Points...	$1,500
(b)	Grade II Silver for 45 Points - doubtful if awarded...........	1,800
(c)	Grade III Gold for 75 Points - doubtful if awarded..........	*

Nr. 77

78. Special Badge for Single-Handed Destruction of a Tank 1942-43
(Sonderabzeichen für das Niederkämpfen von
Panzerkampfwagen durch Einzelkampfer)

(a)   Black class Badge for 1 tank destroyed...................... $175
(b)   Gold class Badge for 5 tanks destroyed   750

Nr. 78a

Nr. 78b   A. Forman

Hauptmann Klaus Coracino

79. Special Badge for Shooting Down Low-Flying Aircraft 1945 (Tieffliegervernichtungsabzeichen)

**Doubtful if badges were awarded, except on paper.

(a)	Black class Badge for 1 plane destroyed....................	*
(b)	Gold class Badge for 5 planes destroyed..................	*

Nr. 79 (post 1945 award)

80. The Snipers Badge 1944-45 (Scharfschützenabzeichen)

(a)	Grade I for 20 Kills....................................	$750
(b)	Grade II for 40 Kills. (Silver Cord)............................	1,250
(c)	Grade III for 60 Kills. (Gold Cord)............................	1,500
Note:	This badge is extremely rare and original examples of the "official" regulation type are rarely seen in collections.	

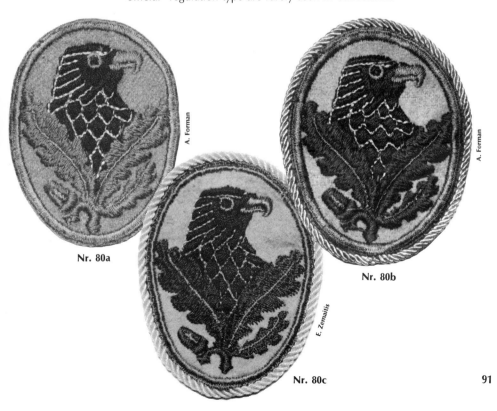

Nr. 80a

Nr. 80b

Nr. 80c

81. Army Bergführer Badge 1936 (Heeresbergführer)

Deluxe convex enamel, pinback.. $1,500

Dr. Klietmann

Nr. 81

General
Eduard Dietl

82. The Armed Forces (Wehrmacht) Wound Badges 1936-1945 (Verwundeten-Abzeichen)

(a) Type A   The so-called Spanish issue, hollow backed WWI style
helmet, embossed with swastika. Variations of manufacture
exist, including deluxe solid type.

(b)		1st Class in Gold. Not awarded during the
		Spanish Civil War $250-350
(c)		2nd Class in Silver. Only one awarded during
		Spanish Civil War 200-250
(d)		3rd Class in Black. Only 182 awarded during
		Spanish Civil War 100-150
	NOTE:	Many examples of this early pattern were made and privately
		purchased after the Spanish Civil War had ended.

Dr. Klietmann

Nr. 82b, c

A. Forman

Nr. 82b, c

A. Forman

Nr. 82d

(e)	Type B	1939 issue with M35 pattern steel helmet design. Early badges are of solid brass or nickel, later types in matt zinc.	
(f)		1st Class in Gold	$90-125
(g)		2nd Class in Silver	60
(h)		3rd Class in Black	20
(i)		Cases or boxes	30-50
(j)		Titled paper packets	20

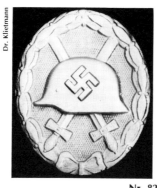
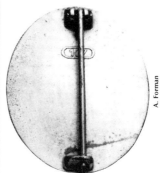

Nr. 82f, g

Nr. 82h

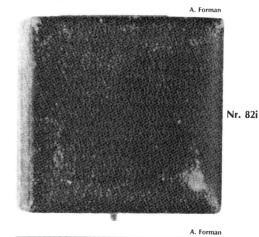

Nr. 82i

**Nr. 82i
(LDO case)**

Nr. 82i
(LDO case)

A. Forman

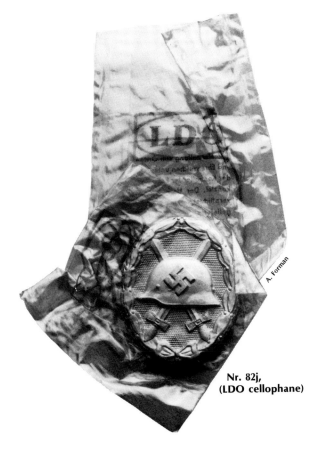

Nr. 82j,
(LDO cellophane)

A. Forman

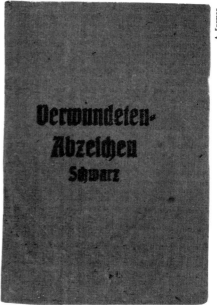

Nr. 82j (silver class LDO packet)   **Nr. 82j (black class packet)**

83. The Wound Badge for 20th July 1944
(Verwundeten-Abz. 20. juli. 1944)

(a)	Gold Class Badge..	$15,000
(b)	Silver Class Badge...	10,000
(c)	Black Class Badge...	10,000
(d)	Cases for all classes	1,000

**Manufactured by C.E. Juncker of Berlin. According to, Dr. K.G.
Klietmann, approx 100 badges struck. All Badges are hallmarked "800"
silver. Badges exist with either "L/12" or "2" on reverse, both maker marks
of C.E. Juncker. Other trial patterns & variants exist.

Nr. 83b

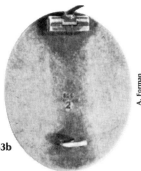

A. Forman

Nr. 83b

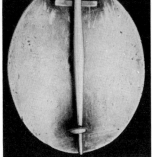

Dr. Klietmann

Nr. 83b

Hermann Historica

Nr. 83d

84. The Armed Forces (Wehrmacht) Drivers Proficiency Badge 1942-45
(Kraftfahr-Bewährungsabzeichen)

(a)	1st Class in Gold...	$25-50
(b)	2nd Class in Silver..	20-30
(c)	3rd Class in Bronze	15-25

Examples issued on cloth backing (Luftwaffe, Navy, & Army) are more scarce than badges with pins. The above prices apply to those with cloth backing.

Nr. 84a

Nr. 84b

Nr. 84c

Nr. 84, reverse

85. Navy U-Boat War Badge 1939
(U-Boots-Kriegsabzeichen)

(a) Type A   Heavy early quality gold-plated tombak issued by
"Schwerin" of Berlin or other makers.
Some Badges unmarked... $200-300

(b) Type B   Later issues in gilt wash on alloy or zinc............................ 100-125

(c)   Titled paper packets or cardboard carton........................ 50-100

Nr. 85a   Dr. Klietmann

Nr. 85c

A. Forman

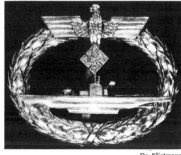

Nr. 86c

Dr. Klietmann

86. Naval U-Boat War Badge with Diamonds
(U-Boots-Kriegsabzeichen mit Brillanten)

(a)   Unique presentation badge awarded to Grand
Admiral Dönitz in solid gold with diamonds inset on
wreath and swastika... *

(b) Type A   Fine quality gold-plated tombak badge by "Schwerin"
of Berlin. With applied silver swastika inset with Brilliants
(Brilliant-cut imitation diamonds).. $10,000

(c) Type B   Fine quality gold-plated silver badge by "Schwerin" of
Berlin. With applied smaller silver swastika inset with
diamonds.. $15,000   **99**

87. Naval U-Boat Combat Clasp 1944-45
(U-Boots-Frontspange)

(a) Type A Heavy quality silver or bronze-plated tombak by "Schwerin"
and "Peekhaus" with flat tapered pin.

(b) Type B Medium weight silvered or bronzed alloy or zinc by "Schwerin"
and "Peekhaus" with fluted tapered pin.

(c) Bronze Class for either bravery or several missions........... $400-450

(d) Silver Class for either bravery or several missions 600

A. Forman

Nr. 87d

88. Naval Destroyers War Badge 1940
(Zerstörer-Kriegsabzeichen)

(a) Type A Heavy quality silver/gold-plated tombak by
"Schwerin" of Berlin $150-200

(b) Type B Medium weight silvered/gilt wash alloy or zinc,
some with maker's marks.. 90-125

(c) Titled paper packet, carton or deluxe case....................... 50-100

Nr. 88b

Dr. Klietmann

89. Naval Destroyers War Badge with Diamonds
(Zerstörer-Kriegsabzeichen mit Brillanten)

**Fine quality gold-plated hallmarked silver badge. Swastika
inset with tiny diamonds ....   *
Only one or two examples known.

E. Liecher

Nr. 89

90. Naval Minesweepers, Sub-Chasers & Escort Vessels War Badge 1940
(Kriegsabzeichen für Minensuch, U-Boots-Jagd, und Sicherungsverbände)

(a)	Type A	Heavy quality silver/gold-plated tombak by "Schwerin" of Berlin $150-200
(b)	Type B	Medium weight silvered/gilt wash alloy or zinc, some with maker's marks....................................... 75-125
(c)		Titled paper packet, carton or deluxe case...................... 50-100

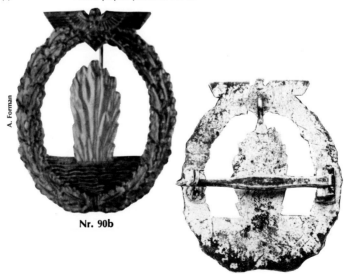

A. Forman

Nr. 90b

91. Naval Minesweepers, Sub-Chasers & Escort Vessels War Badge with Diamonds
(Kriegsabzeichen für Minensuch, U-Boots-Jagd, und Sicherungsverbände mit Brillanten)

**Fine quality gold-plated hallmarked silver badge. Swastika inset with diamonds .... *

Only One or two examples known

Dr. Klietmann

Nr. 91

92. Naval 1st Pattern E-Boat War Badge 1942-43
(Schnellboot-Kriegsabzeichen)

(a)	Type A	Heavy quality silver/gold-plated tombak by "Schwerin" of Berlin	$550
(b)	Type B	Medium weight silvered/gilt wash alloy or zinc, some with maker's marks..	300-400
(c)		Titled paper packet, carton or deluxe case......................	100-150

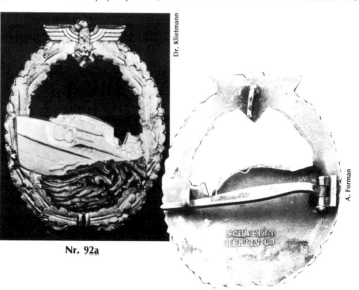

Dr. Klietmann

A. Forman

Nr. 92a

93. Naval 2nd Pattern E-Boat War Badge 1943-45 (Schnellboot-Kriegsabzeichen)

(a) Type A   Heavy quality silver/gilt wash on alloy or zinc by "Schwerin" of Berlin. Rarely found with gilt finish $250

(b) Type B   Heavy quality silver/gilt wash on zinc with makers mark "A.S.", needle pin $250

(c)   Titled paper packet, carton or deluxe case...................... 50-100

Nr. 93b

94. Naval E-Boat War Badge with Diamonds (Schnellboot-Kriegsabzeichen mit Brillanten)

(a) Type A   1st Pattern badge. Fine quality, gold-plated, hallmarked silver badge, Large swastika inset with diamonds... $15,000

(b) Type B   2nd Pattern badge. Fine quality, gold-plated, hallmarked silver badge. Large swastika inset with diamonds... $15,000

**There is at least one original example in gold-plated tombak with swastika inset with imitation stones

Hanseatisches Aukt.

Nr. 94a

Nr. 94b (cut-out swastika)

Nr. 94b
(solid swastika variant)

95. Naval Auxiliary Cruisers War Badge 1941
(Kreigsabzeichen für Hilfskreuzer)

(a) Type A   Heavy quality silver/gold-plated, rivetted badge
by "Schwerin" of Berlin. Some unmarked $200-250

(b) Type B   Mid-war issue gilt wash on alloy or zinc, rivetted 90-150

(c) Type C   Late war issue, gilt wash on grey zinc.
No rivet, needle pin 75-100

(d)   Titled paper packet, carton or deluxe case....................... 50-100

Nr. 95a, Type A,
unmarked

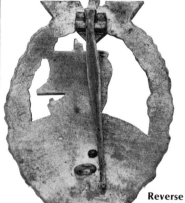

Reverse

96. Naval Auxiliary Cruisers War Badge with Diamonds (Kriegsabzeichen für Hilfskreuzer mit Brillanten)

**Fine quality, gold-plated, hallmarked "900" silver badge. Swastika inset with tiny Brilliants (Brilliant-cut stones examples known with imitation stones or low value diamonds)... $15,000

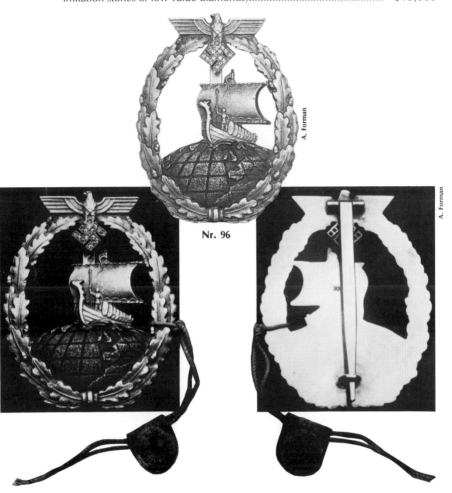

Nr. 96

97. Naval High Seas Fleet War Badge 1941 (Flotten-Kriegsabzeichen)

(a)	Type A	Heavy quality silver/gold-plated tombak by "Adolf Bock"	$250-300
(b)	Type B	Late war issue gilt wash on grey zinc, needle or flat pin...	75-150
(c)		Titled paper packet, carton or deluxe case......................	50-150

Dr. Klietmann

A. Forman

Nr. 97a

A. Forman

WM 723

Flotten-
Kriegsabzeichen

Nr. 97c

98. Naval High Seas Fleet War Badge with Diamonds (Flotten-Kriegsabzeichen mit Brillanten)

**Fine quality, gold-plated, hallmarked silver badge, large swastika inset with tiny diamonds .... *

Only one or two examples known.

Dr. Klietmann

Nr. 98

99. Naval Blockade Runners Badge 1941 (Abzeichen für Blockadebrecher)

(a)	Type A	Early heavy quality, oxidised, silver-plated tombak by "Adolf Bock", wide tapered pin.....................................	$200-250
(b)	Type B	Heavy oxidised, silvered alloy, needle pin some with makers marks..	150
(c)		Large blue case for badge and miniature stickpin	100
(d)		Blue case for badge	75
(e)		Large half-size miniature of badge on stickpin	100

Dr. Klietmann

Nr. 99b

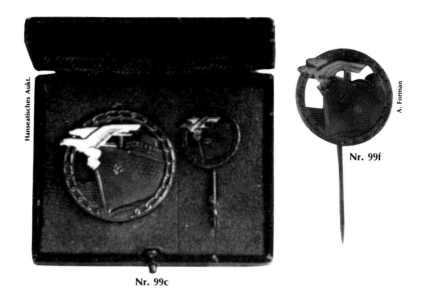

Nr. 99c

Nr. 99f

A. Forman (right side)

Hanseatisches Aukt. (left side)

100. Naval Coastal Artillery War Badge 1941 (Kriegsabzeichen für die Marine Artillerie)

(a)	Type A	Early quality gold-plated tombak badge by "Schwerin" of Berlin. Tapered pin $150-200
(b)	Type B	Late war issue in alloy or zinc, needle pin........................ 60-90
(c)	Type C	Variation, "Small Eagle" type... 150
(d)		Titled paper packet, carton or deluxe case....................... 50-150

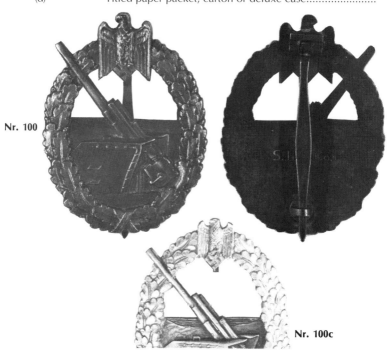

Nr. 100

Nr. 100c

108

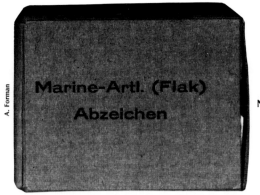

A. Forman

Marine-Artl. (Flak) Abzeichen

Nr. 100d

101. Naval Combat Clasp 1944-45 (Marine-Frontspange)

(a) Type A Crude hand-crafted originals (variations) $300-450
(b) Type B Manufacturer's samples in tombak
            Some maker marked 400-500
(c) Type C Protoype design badge in tombak 1,500

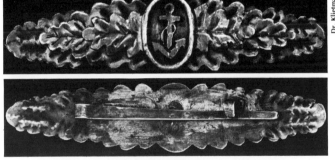

Dr. Klietmann

Nr. 101a

Dr. Klietmann

Nr. 101c

102. Naval Combat Badge of the Small Battle Units(K-Men)1943 (Kampfabzeichen der Kleinkampfmittel)

(a)   7th Class, gold metal clasp (not awarded) .... *
(b)   6th Class, silver metal clasp (not awarded)......................... *
(c)   5th Class, bronze metal clasp (doubtful if awarded)......... * **109**

Dr. Klietmann

Nr. 102a, b, c

(d)	4th Class, cloth patch (3 swords)...	$350
(e)	3rd Class, cloth patch (2 swords)...	300
(f)	2nd Class, cloth patch (1 sword)...	250
(g)	1st Class, cloth patch (no swords)......................................	250
(h)	Qualification Swordfish Badge, cloth patch (Bewährungsabzeichen)...	200

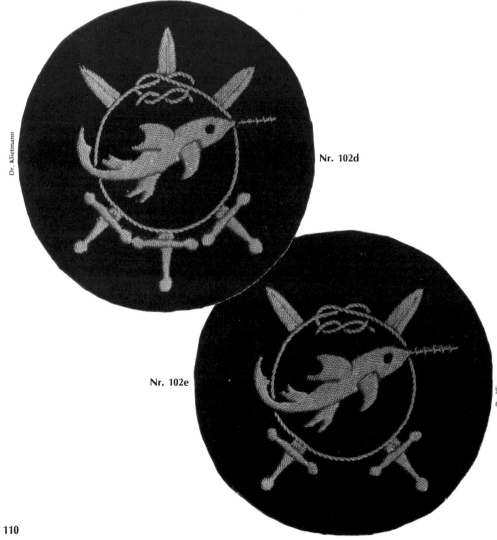

Dr. Klietmann

Nr. 102d

Nr. 102e

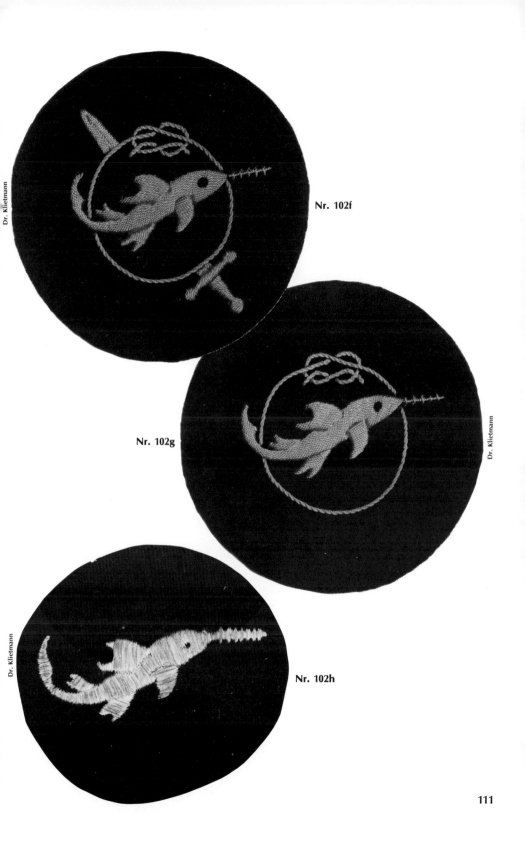

Nr. 102f

Nr. 102g

Nr. 102h

Dr. Klietmann

Dr. Klietmann

Dr. Klietmann

103. Naval Dockyard Workers Achievement Badges (Werft-Leistungs-Abzeichen)

(a) Type A   "Norway" Naval Dockyard service issue lapel badge in zinc, depicts Naval surface vessel within cog & surmounted by a stylised eagle-swastika... $400

(b) Type B   "U-Boat" (West France) Naval Dockyard service issue lapel badge, 1st issue in bronze.. 300

(c)   "U-Boat"(West France)Naval Dockyard service issue lapel badge, 2nd issue in alloy or zinc.. 250

**Both Type A and Type B were awarded with a certificate

Nr. 103a

C. v. Tettinck

Malvoux

Nr. 103b
(bronze)

Malvoux

Nr. 103c
(white metal)

104. Naval Cloth-Active Service - War Badges c. 1941-42

   (a)   Type A   Officers bullion type.. $200-300

   (b)   Type B   Other ranks' type in cotton.. 100-200

Cotton embroidered
type of Nr. 88
(Destroyer)

Cotton embroidered type
of Nr. 97 (Fleet War Service)

Cotton embroidered
type of Nr. 90
(Minesweeper)

Cotton embroidered
type of Nr. 92 (E-Boat,
1st pattern)

105. Luftwaffe 1st Pattern Pilot/Observers Badge 1935 (Gemeinsames Flugzeugführer-und Beobachterabzeichen)

Examples exist by "Juncker" and "Godet" of Berlin.

(a) Type A   Deluxe type with broad flat pin, "Godet" marked $2,500

(b) Type B   Fine quality nickel silver, needle pin type, maker marked   1,800

(c)   Titled blue case   500

Dr. Klietmann

Nr. 105a

Nr. 105b

Nr. 105c

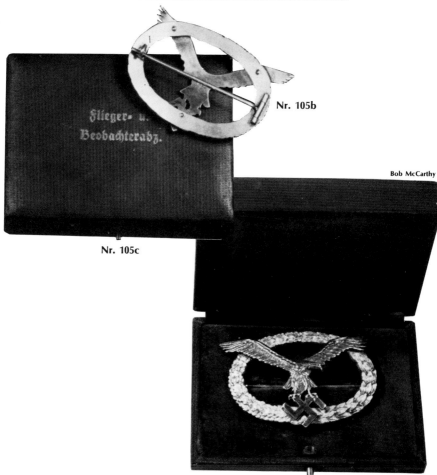

Bob McCarthy

106. Luftwaffe Pilots Badge 1936-45
(Flugzeugführerabzeichen)

(a)	Type A	Early quality plated type..	$400
(b)	Type B	War-time issues...	300
(c)	Type C	Very late war issues in alloy or zinc (crude)	150
(d)	Type D	Variant Rounded-wreath design in nickel silver...............	500
(e)		Titled blue case..	100-150
(f)		Titled carton	75

Dr. Klietmann

Nr. 106b

A. Forman

Nr. 106c

C. v. Tettinck

Nr. 106d

Nr. 106f

Nr. 106e

107. Luftwaffe Observers Badge 1936-45 (Beobachterabzeichen)

(a)	Type A	Early quality plated type	$400
(b)	Type B	War-time issues in alloy	300
(c)	Type C	Very late war issues in zinc (crude)	150
(d)		Titled blue case	100-150

Nr. 107a,
Type A

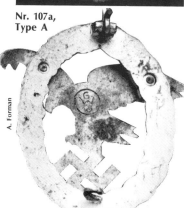

Nr. 107d

108. Luftwaffe Combined Pilot/Observer Badge 1936-45
(Gemeinsames Flugzeugführer-und Beobachter-Abzeichen)

(a)	Type A	Early quality plated/tombak type, some maker marked..	$750-900
(b)	Type B	War-time issues in alloy	600
(c)	Type C	Very late war issues marked "A" in zinc	400
(d)		Titled blue case	150-200

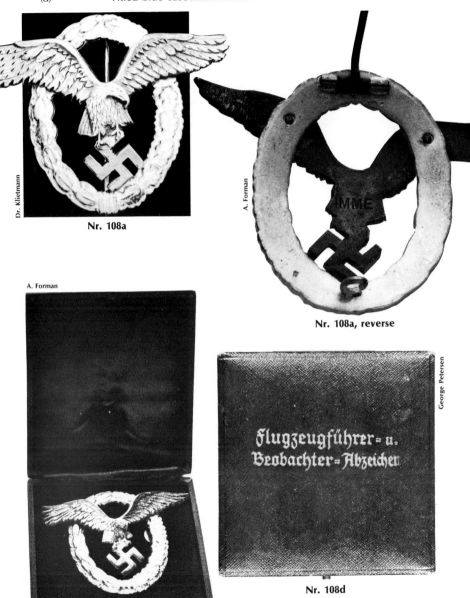

Dr. Klietmann

Nr. 108a

A. Forman

IMME

Nr. 108a, reverse

A. Forman

George Petersen

Flugzeugführer = u.
Beobachter=Abzeichen

Nr. 108d

109. Luftwaffe Special Combined Pilot/Observer Badge with Diamonds

(Gemeinsames Flugzeugführer-und Beobachter-Abzeichen in Gold mit Brillanten)

(a) Type A Actual award badge in solid gold & platinum, of superb quality when compared to other "Brilliants" awards $20,000

(b) Type B Official awarded dress copy in silver/gilt by "Rudolf Stubiger" of Vienna 12,500

(c)   Deluxe presentation case .... *

**Nr. 109a,
Type A**

C.E. Campion

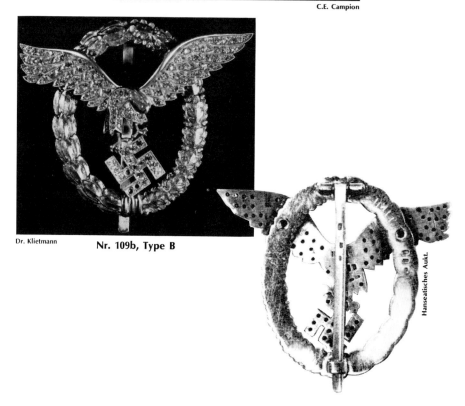

Dr. Klietmann   **Nr. 109b, Type B**

Hanseatisches Aukt.

110. Luftwaffe Wireless Operator/Air Gunners Badge 1936-45 (Fliegerschützenabzeichen für Bordfunker)

(a)	Type A	Early quality plated/tombak type	$300-400
(b)	Type B	War-time issues in alloy	200
(c)	Type C	Late war issues (solid swastika detail) in zinc	150
(d)		Titled Blue Case	100-150

Nr. 110a

A. Forman

Nr. 110c

George Petersen

Nr. 110d

George Petersen

Nr. 110d
(variations in
lettering exist)

George Petersen

Nr. 110d,
titled box

111. Luftwaffe Air Gunners/Flight Engineers Badge 1942-45 (Fliegerschützenabzeichen für Bordschützen u. Bordmechaniker)

(a)	Type A	Early quality plated badge c. 1942	$400-500
(b)	Type B	War-time issues in alloy 1943..	300
(c)	Type C	Late war issue in zinc 1944-45 (solid swastika detail).......	200
(d)	Type D	Badge for Unqualified Gunners 1944. Black wreath, silver swastika & silver eagle. In alloy or zinc	750
(e)		Titled blue case..	125-175

Dr. Klietmann

A. Forman

Nr. 111a

Nr. 111c

George Petersen

Nr. 111e

Nr. 111d
(unqualified)

C. v. Tettinck

112. Luftwaffe Glider Pilot Badge 1940
(Segelflugzeugführerabzeichen)

George Petersen

A. Forman

Nr. 112b

Segel=
Flugzeugführer=
Abzeichen

Nr. 112d

George Petersen

121

113. Luftwaffe Fliers Commemorative Badge 1936-45
(Flieger-Erinneurungsabzeichen)

(a)	Type A	Early quality plated badge by "Juncker" of Berlin............	$2,000
(b)	Type B	War-time issue plated alloy..	800
(c)	Type C	Late war issue (solid swastika detail) in zinc......................	500
(d)		Titled blue case..	300-400

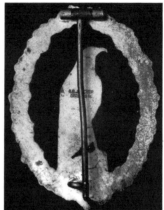

Nr. 113a

Nr. 113d

114. Luftwaffe Flak War Badge 1941-45
(Flak-Kampfabzeichen der Luftwaffe)

(a)	Type A	Early quality plated badge with maker's mark..................	$150-200
(b)	Type B	Late war issue in alloy or zinc	85-110
(c)		Titled black carton box...	100
(d)		Titled blue case	125-150

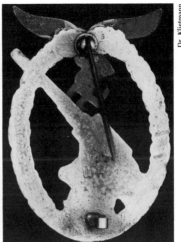

Dr. Klietmann

Nr. 114a

George Petersen

Flak-
Kampf-
Abz.

Nr. 114d

Nr. 114c, titled box

George Petersen

123

115. Luftwaffe Ground Combat Badge 1942-45
(Erdkampfabzeichen der Luftwaffe)

(a)	Type A	Early quality plated badge by "M.u. K"(two-part)	$175-225
(b)	Type B	Middle war-time issue (two-part) in plated alloy	100-150
(c)	Type C	Late war issue (one-part) in zinc	75
(d)		Titled blue case	200-250

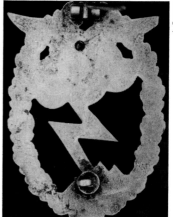

A. Forman

Nr. 115a

George Petersen

Nr. 115d

116. Luftwaffe Special Grade Ground Combat Badge 1944-45
(Erdkampfabzeichen der Luftwaffe - Sonder Klasse)

(a)		Grade II for 25 Engagements	*
(b)		Grade III for 50 Engagements	*
(c)		Grade IV for 75 Engagements	*
(d)		Grade V for 100 Engagements	*

**Badges were manufactured, but doubtful if awarded.

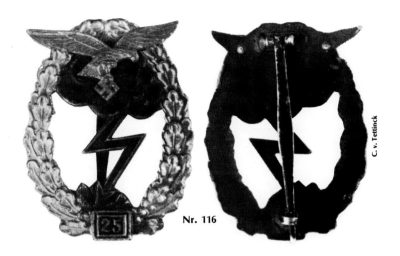

Nr. 116

C. v. Tettinck

117. Luftwaffe Tank Battle Badge & Special Grade Badges in Silver 1944-45
(Panzerkampf Abzeichen der Luftwaffe-im silber)

(a)	Tank Battle Badge in silver-unnumbered	$1,250
(b)	Grade II for 25 Engagements	*
(c)	Grade III for 50 Engagements	*
(d)	Grade IV for 75 Engagements	*
(e)	Grade V for 100 Engagements	*

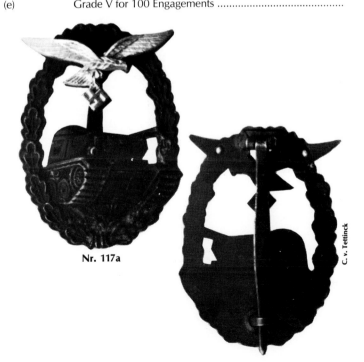

Nr. 117a

C. v. Tettinck

Nr. 117a,
one-piece, zinc variant

Luftwaffe Tank Battle Badge & Special Grade Badges in Black 1944-45
(Panzerkampf Abzeichen der Luftwaffe-im schwarz)

(f)   Tank Battle Badge in black-unnumbered........................ $1,500
(g)   Grade II for 25 Engagements... *
(h)   Grade III for 50 Engagements.. *
(i)   Grade IV for 75 Engagements.. *
(j)   Grade V for 100 Engagements .... *

**Badges were manufactured, but doubtful if any but a handful of the basic Grade I (un-numbered) were awarded.

118. Luftwaffe Sea Battle Badge 1944
(Seekampfabzeichen der Luftwaffe)

**Doubtful if manufactured except in trial pattern form, although instiued on 27 November 1944 and illustrated/described in the Luftwaffe Verordnungs-blatt.. *

Wartime illustration, LVBl 1945

119. Luftwaffe Close Combat Clasp 1944
(Nahkampfspange der Luftwaffe)

(a)   Class I bronze .... *
(b)   Class II silver .... *
(c)   Class III gold .... *

**Only a few badges were manufactured. Documented awards known.

Wartime illustration, LVBl 1944

120. Luftwaffe Parachütists Badge 1936-45
(Fallschirmschützenabzeichen)

(a) Type A   Early quality plated tomback badge with
               maker's mark $250-350
(b) Type B   War-time issues plated alloy 175-250
(c) Type C   Late war issues in zinc, etc 125-175
(d)   Titled paper packet or carton 75-100
(e)   Titled blue case 100-150

NOTE: Luftwaffe personnel utilized cloth versions of their war badges more than any other branch of service, variations of which are illustrated below.

(a)   Officers bullion types $250-500
(b)   Other ranks' types in cotton 50-150

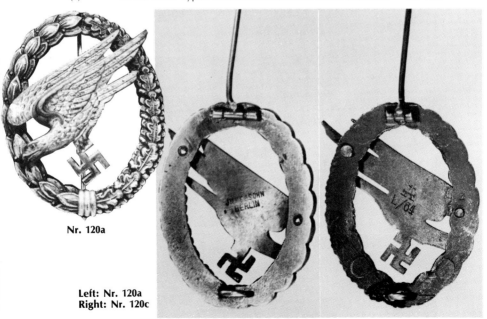

Nr. 120a

Left: Nr. 120a
Right: Nr. 120c

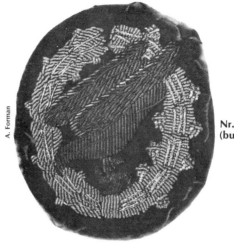

A. Forman

Nr. 120
(bullion)

George Petersen

Fallschirmschützen

George Petersen

Fallschirmschützen=
Abzeichen

George Petersen

Fallschirmschützen=
Abzeichen

F. W. ASSMANN & SOHNE,
Lüdenscheid

**Three variations of the case (Nr. 120d)
for the Parachutist Badge.**

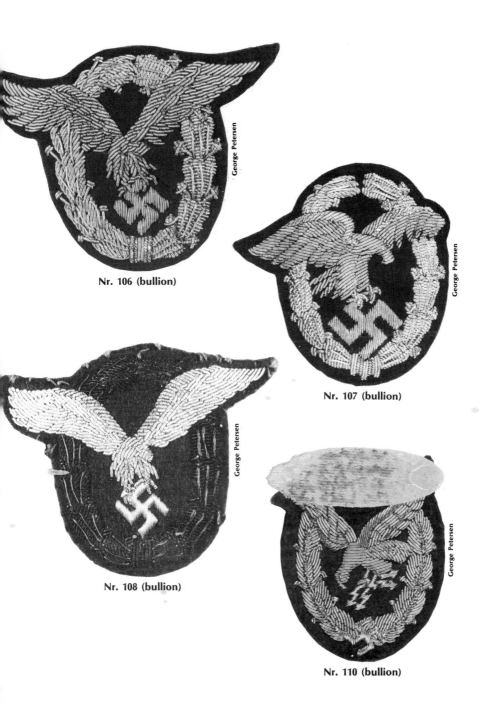

Nr. 106 (bullion)

George Petersen

Nr. 107 (bullion)

George Petersen

Nr. 108 (bullion)

George Petersen

Nr. 110 (bullion)

George Petersen

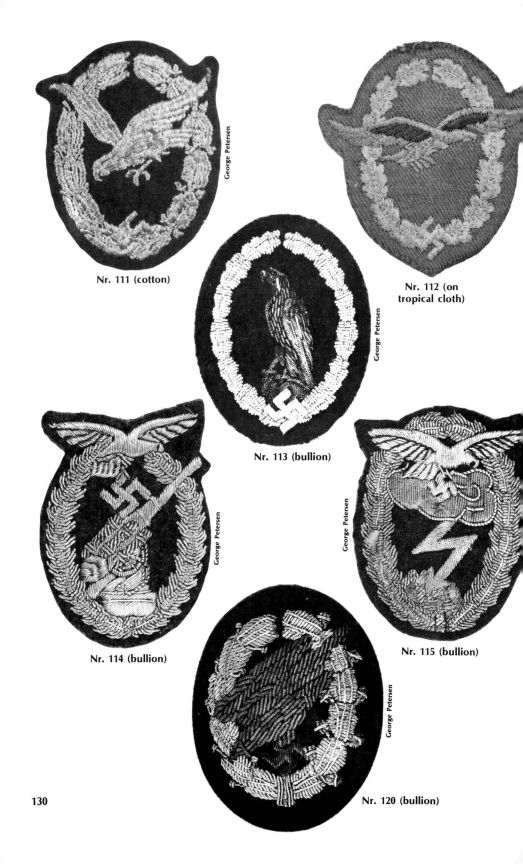

Nr. 111 (cotton)

Nr. 112 (on
tropical cloth)

Nr. 113 (bullion)

Nr. 114 (bullion)

Nr. 115 (bullion)

Nr. 120 (bullion)

George Petersen

121. Luftwaffe Day Fighter Clasp 1941-45
(Frontflugspange für Jäger)

(a)	Gold Class with Pendant (numbered missions)	$650-850
(b)	Gold Class with Pendant (flower design)	550-700
(c)	Gold Class	400-500
(d)	Silver Class	300-350
(e)	Bronze Class	250-300
(f)	Titled blue case	150-200

Prices apply to only early quality clasps, late war issues in zinc (crude) would be priced at 30% less.

Nr. 121b

A. Forman

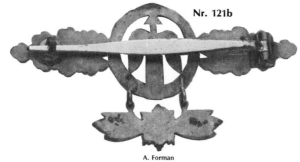

Nr. 121a with "1500" pendant

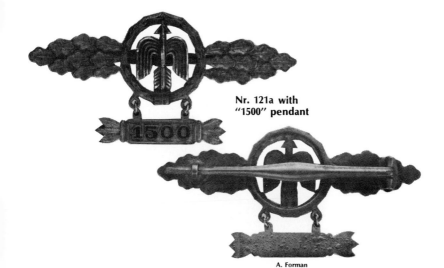

A. Forman

131

A. Forman

Nr. 121d

A. Forman

A. Forman

Nr. 121e

George Petersen

Frontflugspange

für

Jäger

Silber

Left: Titled packet for Nr. 121, silver class
Below: Titled case for Nr. 121, gold class

Frontflugspange
für Jäger
gold

George Petersen

122. Luftwaffe Night Fighter Clasp 1941-45(black wreath) (Frontflugspange für Nachtjäger)

(a)	Gold Class with Pendant (numbered missions)	$800-900
(b)	Gold Class with Pendant (flower design)	700-800
(c)	Gold Class	600
(d)	Silver Class	450
(e)	Bronze Class	350
(f)	Titled blue case	200-250

Prices apply to only early quality clasps, late war issues in zinc (crude) would be priced at 30% less.

Nr. 122a

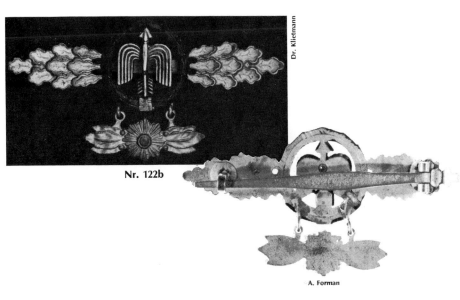

Nr. 122b

A. Forman

A. Forman

Nr. 122c

Dr. Klietmann

Nr. 122e

123. Luftwaffe Long-Range Day Fighters & Air-to-Ground Support Squadrons Clasp 1941-44 (Downward Arrow)
(Frontflugspange für Zerstörer und Schlachtflieger)

(a)	Gold Class with Pendant (numbered missions)	$900-1,200
(b)	Gold Class with Pendant (flower design)	800-1,000
(c)	Gold Class	700
(d)	Silver Class	550
(e)	Bronze Class	450
(f)	Titled Blue Cases	200-300

Prices apply to only early quality clasps, late war issues, in zinc (crude) would be priced at 20% less.

Dr. Klietmann

Nr. 123a

A. Forman

Nr. 123b

Nr. 123d   Dr. Klietmann

124. Luftwaffe Long-Range Night Fighter & Night Intruder Squadrons Clasp 1941-45 (black wreath). (Downward Arrow) (Frontflugspange für Fernnachtjäger)

(a)	Gold Class with Pendant (numbered missions)	$900-1,200
(b)	Gold Class with Pendant (flower design)	850-1,000
(c)	Gold Class	750-800
(d)	Silver Class	600
(e)	Bronze Class	500
(f)	Titled blue case	250-300

Prices apply to only early quality clasps, late war issues, in zinc (crude) would be priced at 20% less.

George Petersen

Nr. 124a

125. Luftwaffe Heavy/Medium & Dive Bombers Squadron Clasp (Frontflugspange für Kampfflieger)

(a)	Gold Class with Pendant (numbered missions)	$550-700
(b)	Gold Class with Pendant (flower design)	450-600
(c)	Gold Class	400
(d)	Silver Class	300
(e)	Bronze Class	200
(f)	Titled blue case	100-150

Prices apply to only early quality clasps, late war issues in zinc would be priced at 30% less.

A. Forman

Nr. 125b

A. Forman

Nr. 125c

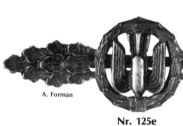

A. Forman

Nr. 125e

Dr. Klietmann

Nr. 125d, reverse

George Petersen

Frontflugspange
für Kampfflieger
filber

Nr. 125f, silver class

126. Luftwaffe Reconnaissance, Air/Sea Rescue & Meteorological Clasp
(Frontflugspange für Aufklärer)

(a)   Gold Class with Pendant(numbered missions)................. $600-700

(b)   Gold Class with Pendant(flower design)........................... 500-600

(c)   Gold Class 450

(d)   Silver Class 350

(e)   Bronze Class.. 250

(f)   Titled blue case 100-150

*Prices apply to only early quality clasps, late war issues, in zinc would be priced at some 30% less.

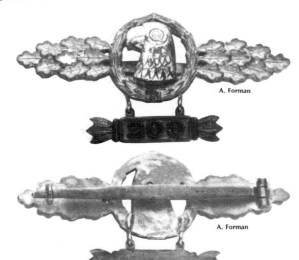

A. Forman

A. Forman

Nr. 126a

A. Forman

Nr. 126b

A. Forman

Nr. 126c

A. Forman

Nr. 126d

Dr. Klietmann

A. Forman

Nr. 126e

Frontflugspange
für Aufklärer
silber

A. Forman

Nr. 126f, silver class

Frontflugspange
für Aufklärer
gold

George Petersen

Nr. 126f, gold class

127. Luftwaffe Transport & Glider Squadron Clasp
(Frontflugspange für Transportflieger)

(a)	Gold Class with Pendant (numbered missions)	$600-700
(b)	Gold Class with Pendant (flower design)	500-600
(c)	Gold Class	450
(d)	Silver Class	350
(e)	Bronze Class	250
(f)	Titled blue case	100-150

Prices apply to only early quality clasps, late war issue in zinc would be priced at 30% less.

A. Forman

Nr. 127a

A. Forman

Nr. 127c

A. Forman

Dr. Klietmann

Nr. 127e

George Petersen

Nr. 127f, titled packet for gold class with pendant

128. Luftwaffe Air-to-Ground Support Squadron Clasp 1944-45 (Frontflugspange für Schlachtflieger)

(a)	Gold Class with Pendant (numbered missions)	$1,000-1,200
(b)	Gold Class	750-900
(c)	Silver Class	550
(d)	Bronze Class	400
(e)	Titled blue case	250-300
(f)	Special presentation solid gold clasp with Brilliants - Awarded for "2000" Missions. Unique award to Luft. Ace, Oberst Rudel	

Prices apply to quality clasps, later war issues in zinc, (crude) woud be priced at 20% less.

Dr. Klietmann

Nr. 128a

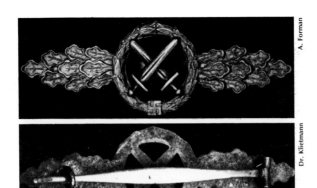

Nr. 128c

Nr. 128d

Nrs. 121-128 pendants
(numbered missions)

Nr. 128f, Oberst Rudel's unique gold and diamond clasp for "2000" missions

NOTE: Luftwaffe personnel utilized bullion versions of the Frontflugspange. Todate, the only variations observed are as follows:

(a)   Fighter Clasp $500
(b)   Bomber Clasp 500
(c)   Reconnaissance Clasp 500

George Petersen

Nr. 125 (bullion)

Oblt. Martin Meisel wears a bullion version of the Reconnaissance Clasp and Iron Cross 1st Class.

129. Luftwaffe Goblet of Honour - for outstanding achievement (Ehrenpokal für Besondere Leistung im Luftkrieg)

(a)	1st type in hallmarked "835" silver by "Wagner" of Berlin	$3,000
(b)	2nd type in Alpaka silver-plate by "Wagner" of Berlin ...	2,000
(c)	1st type red leather shaped case	*
(d)	2nd type blue leatherette box-case	750

Always engraved with recipents name, rank & date.

Nr. 129

D. Littlejohn

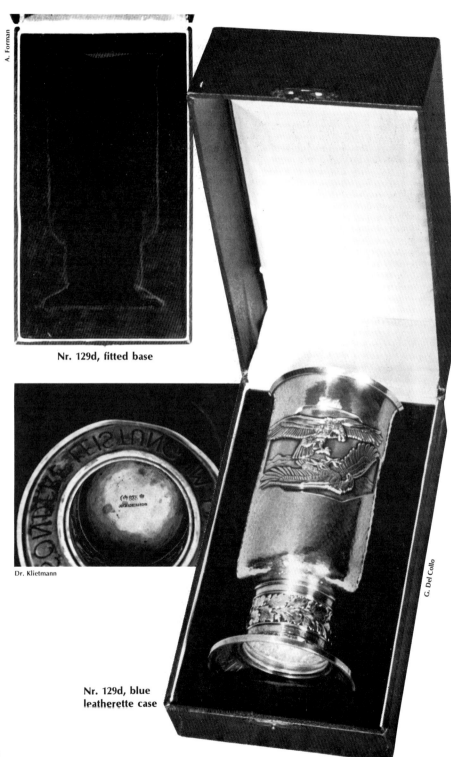

A. Forman

Nr. 129d, fitted base

Dr. Klietmann

G. Del Collo

Nr. 129d, blue
leatherette case

130. Luftwaffe Salver of Honour - for distinguished achievements in action 1942-45
(Ehrenschale für Herorragende Kampfleistungen)

(a)   Fine quality alpaka silverplate by "Wagner" of Berlin $6,000

(b)   Large presentation case ....   *

Always engraved with recipents bame, rank, and date.

Dr. Klietmann

Nr. 130a

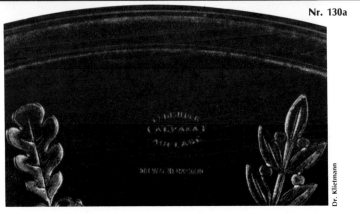

Dr. Klietmann

131. Luftwaffe Silvered Large Medallion for Outstanding Achievements in the Technical Branch of the Air Force
(Medaille "für Ausgezeichnete Leistungen im Technischen Dienst der Luftwaffe)

(a)	Medallion, 75mm, silver-plated		$300
(b)	Black case		150

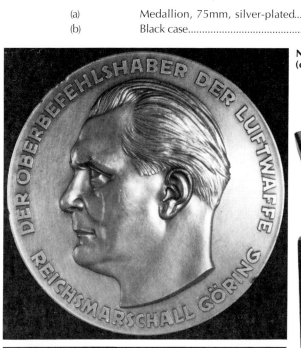

Nr. 131a
(obverse)

A. Forman

Nr. 131b

Nr. 131a
(reverse)

Dr. Klietmann

132. **Luftwaffe Air District West France Medallion for Meritorious Achievements**

(Feldluftgaukommando Westfrankreich Luftgauplakette für Treue Dienstleistungen)

(a)   Bronze, 41mm... $350
(b)   Miniature (half size) lapel badge, 20mm.......................... 250

Nr. 132a (obverse)   Nr. 132a (reverse)

133. **Luftwaffe Air District Belgium-Northern France Medallion for Meritorious Achievements**

(Luftgaukommando Belgien-Nordfrankreich Luftgauplakette für Treue Dienstleistungen)

(a)   Bronze, 41mm... $350

Nr. 133a (obverse)   Nr. 133a (reverse)

134. **Luftwaffe Plaque for Outstanding Achievement & Merit in the 21st Air Force Field Division 1942**

(Plakette für Hervorragende Leistungen und Verdienste im 21. Luftwaffen Felddivision)

(a)   Cast iron plaque $450   **147**

Nr. 134a

Dr. Klietmann

Dr. Klietmann

George Petersen

Nr. 135a

Nr. 135a,
variant

148

135. **Luftwaffe Plaque for Special Achievement in the Air District Norway**
        (Plakette für Besondere Leistung im Luftgau Norwegen)

    (a)   Bronzed color, cast iron (local manufacture)................... $400

136. **Luftwaffe Plaque for the Southeast Command of the Air Force**
        (Luftwaffenkommando "Südost" Plakette)

    (a)   Bronze plaque.. $500

Nr. 136a

137. **Luftwaffe Plaque for Outstanding Technical Achievements in the Southern Command**
        (Plakette für Hervoragende Technische Leistungen im Suden)

    (a)   Cast-iron plaque... $400

Nr. 137a

149

138. Luftwaffe G.O. Air District Staff Finlands Plaque for Proof of Merit 1943

(Der Kommandierende General des Luftgau-Stabes, Finnland, "für Besondere Bewährung)

(a)   Bronze plaque (reverse numbered) $400

Nr. 138a

139. Luftwaffe Plaque for Outstanding Achievement in Air District XI
(Plakette "für Hervorrangende Leistung im Luftgau XI")

(a)	1st Type-cast bronze..	$450
(b)	2nd Type-bronzed metal-bronze class............................	350
(c)	2nd Type-silvered metal-silver class..............................	400

Engraved with recipients name and rank.

140. Luftwaffe Shield for Special Merit in the Battle of Crete 1941

(Schild für Besondere Verdienste im Einsatz Kreta 1941 der Kommandierende General des XI Fliegerkorps)

(a) Type A   Luftwaffe eagle emblem Bronze plaque.
(In Anerkennung Besonderer Verdienste im
einsatz Kreta verleich ich dieses Schild dem)................. $750

(b) Type B   Luftwaffe Parachutist diving eagle emblem
(no swastika), Bronze plaque 650

Dr. Klietmann

Nr. 139a,
1st Type

George Petersen

Nr. 139a,
variant

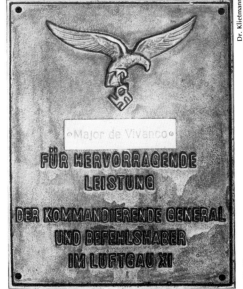

Dr. Klietmann

Nr. 139a,
variant

Nr. 139b,
2nd Type

Col. K. Farnes

Nr. 140b

141. Armed Forces Long Service Awards
(Wehrmacht-Dienstauszeichenungen)

(a)	Silver Medal for 4 years	$40
(b)	Gold Medal for 12 years	60
(c)	Silver Cross for 18 years	150
(d)	Gold Cross for 25 years	200
(e)	Gold Cross & Oakleaf Emblem for 40 years	350
(f)	Paper packets for 4 & 12 year medals	50
(g)	Green carton for 18 year cross	75
(h)	Green case for 25 & 40 year crosses	100-150

Above applies only to awards complete with eagle-emblems on original ribbons. Luftwaffe issue, add 20% to price.

Nr. 140a and b, 4 and 12 year medals mounted as worn (Luftwaffe issue)

Nr. 141a

Nr. 141b

Nr. 141c   Nr. 141c, reverse

Nr. 141c as worn

Nr. 141d (Luftwaffe issue)

Dr. Klietmann

Nr. 141e

Nr. 141e (Luftwaffe issue)

Political and Civil Orders, Decorations and Medals 1933~1945

142. Meritorious Order of the German Eagle 1937-1945
(Verdienstorden vom Deutschen Adler)

	**In 1937 the 1st Model, without "Fan" suspender, was awarded for only a few months. Any classes of this extremely rare type are worth 50% more than any catalogue price shown.	
(a)	Grand Cross sash cross and 8-pointed breast star set	$6,000
(b)	As above but with Swords 1939-43 (mit Schwertern).	7,000
(c)	Large red leather titled case	1,250

Dr. Klietmann

Early, solid style Breast Star

Nrs. 142a, 150a, 151a & 152a

Nrs. 142a, 150a, 151a & 152a

Dr. Klietmann

Note:
First form Breast Stars are the massive, solid, heavy type with lead-ball rivets. The later second form are fluted, convex and lightweight with open domed rivets.

Dr. Klietmann

Nrs. 142b, 150b, 151b & 152b

157

Nrs. 142b, 150b, 151b & 152b

Dr. Klietmann

Dr. Klietmann

Nrs. 142a, 150a, 151a & 152a - Sash Badge, early with no suspension fan.

Dr. Klietmann

Nrs. 142b, 150b, 151b & 152b - Sash Badge with Swords

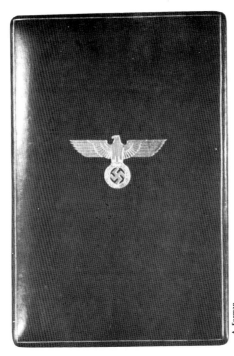

Nrs. 142c, 150c, 151c
& 152c, set case

A. Forman

143. Special Class Golden Grand Cross Set 1939 (Sonderstufe)

(a)   Grand Cross Set in Gold...   *
(b)   Large red leather titled case.......................................   *
    **Approximately 16 awarded

Nr. 143a
(in Gold)

Dr. Klietmann

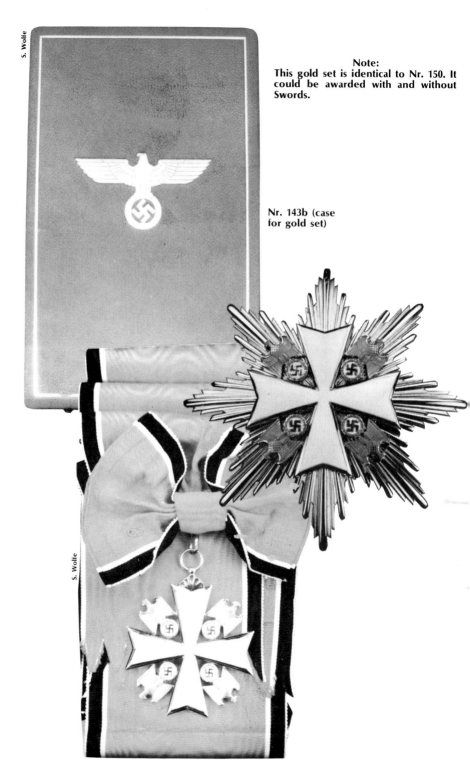

S. Wolfe

Note:
This gold set is identical to Nr. 150. It could be awarded with and without Swords.

Nr. 143b (case for gold set)

S. Wolfe

Nr. 143a (gold)

144. Unique Special Grade of Grand Cross Set with Diamonds 1937 ("Sonderstufe mit Brillanten")

(a)   Awarded to Mussolini by Hitler on his State Visit in 1937   *

(b)   Large red leather titled case..   *

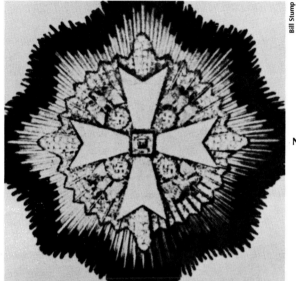

Bill Stump

Nr. 144a

Mussolini wears his "Grand Cross of the German Eagle Order with Diamonds" (Nr. 144) during Hitler's state visit to Italy in May 1938.

145. Order of the German Eagle with Star 1937-39
(Deutsche Adlerorden mit stern)

(a)	Neck Cross (50mm) & 6-pointed Breast Star (75mm).....	$4,000
(b)	Large red leather titled case..	700
(c)	As above, but with Swords (mit Schwertern)...................	4,500
(d)	Large red leather titled case..	700

Nrs. 145a & 146a

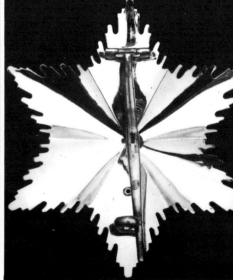

Dr. Klietmann

Nrs. 145a & 153a

Dr. Klietm

Nrs. 145b & d - 1937 issue case is without gold border on lid.

Later version with gold border on lid.

Nrs. 145c, 146b, 153b & 154b

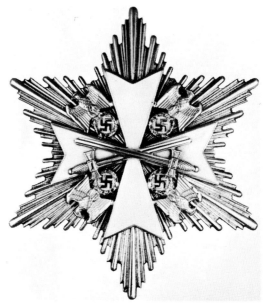

Nrs. 145c & 153b

146. Order of the German Eagle 1st Class Neck Cross 1937-43
(Deutsche Adlerorden, Erste Stufe)

(a)		Neck Cross (50mm)	$1,600
(b)		As above but with Swords (mit Schwertern)	1,800
(c)		Large red leather titled case	600

Nrs. 146a & b,
154a & b

A. Forman

147. Order of the German Eagle, 2nd Class Pin-back Breast Star 1937-43

(Deutsche Adlerorden, zweite Stufe)

(a)　　　　Pin-back Cross (45mm).. $1,250
(b)　　　　As above but with Swords (mit Schwertern).................... 1,400
(c)　　　　Small red leather titled case.. 500

Nr. 147a

Nr. 147b

Nr. 147a & b

Nr. 147a, cased

165

E. Zemaitis

Nr. 147b with Swords and outer case

148. Order of the German Eagle, 3rd Class Breast Cross 1937-43 (Deutsche Adlerorden, Dritte Stufe)

(a)		Breast Cross (45mm)	$1,100
(b)		As above, but with Swords (mit Schwertern)	1,250
(c)		Small red leather titled case	450

Dr. Klietmann

Nr. 148a

Nr. 148a & b case

A. Forman

P. Bradley

Nr. 148a, cased

149. Order of the German Eagle, Medals of Merit 1937-45 (Deutsche Verdienst Medaille)

(a)	1st Type silver medal 1937-43 (Gothic script)..................	$500
(b)	As above, but with Swords (mit Schwertern)....................	600
(c)	Small red leather titled cases..	300
(d)	2nd Type silver medal 1943-45 (Latin script)...................	800
(e)	As above, but with Swords (mit Schwertern)....................	1,000
(f)	Small red leather titled cases..	350
(g)	2nd Type bronze medal 1943-45 (Latin script)................	300
(h)	As above, but with Swords (mit Schwertern)....................	350
(i)	Titled paper packets..	150

Nr. 149a & d   Nr. 149b & c

Nr. 149 case

Nr. 149a & b,
reverse

Nr. 149d,
reverse

Nr. 149g

Nr. 149e,
reverse

Nr. 149g,
reverse

150. Grand Cross of the Order of the German Eagle in Gold 1943-45 (Goldenes Grosskreuz des Deutchen Adlerordens)

(a)	Sash Cross (66mm) & 8-pointed Breast Star (90mm)......	*
(b)	As above, but with Swords (mit Schwertern)....................	*
(c)	Large red leather titled case..	*

(Same as Nr. 143, in Gold)

Von Ribbentrop wears his Grand Cross of the Order of the German Eagle in Gold.

151. Grand Cross of the Order of the German Eagle 1943-45 (Grosskreuz des Deutschen Adlerordens)

(a)	Sash Cross (60mm) & 8-pointed Breast Star (80mm)......	$5,500
(b)	As above, but with Swords (mit Schwertern)....................	6,000
(c)	Large red leather titled case..	1,250

(Same as Nr. 142)

152. Order of the German Eagle, 1st Class Set 1943-45
(Deutsche Adlerorden Erste Klasse)

(a)	Sash Cross (50mm) & 8-pointed Breast Star (80mm)......	$4,500
(b)	As above, but with Swords (mit Schwertern)....................	5,000
(c)	Large red leather titled case..	1,000

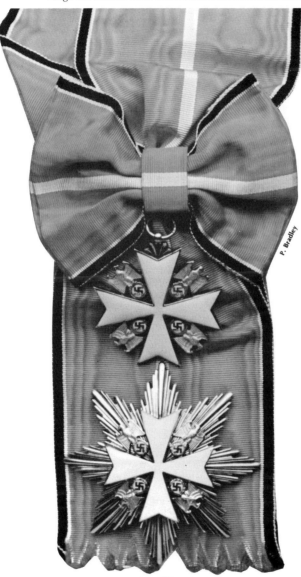

Nr. 152a
(only class with silver eagles)

Nr. 152c

P. Bradley

Nr. 152a,
cased set

153. Order of the German Eagle, 2nd Class Set 1943-45
(Deutsche Adlerorden Zweite Klasse)

(a)	Neck Cross (50mm) & 6-pointed Breast Star (75mm).....	$3,500
(b)	As above, but with Swords (mit Schwertern)...................	4,000
(c)	Large red leather titled case..	700

Nr. 153c

Nr. 153a,
cased set

P. Bradley

154. Order of the German Eagle, 3rd Class 1943-45
(Deutsche Adlerorden Dritte Klasse)

(a)	Neck Cross (50mm)	$1,400
(b)	As above, but with Swords (mit Schwertern)	1,700
(c)	Large red leather titled case	600

Nr. 154a, also Nr. 153a

Nr. 154c case
for neck cross

A. Forman

155. Order of the German Eagle, 4th Class 1943-45
(Deutsche Adlerorden Vierte Klasse)

(a)	Breast Cross, pin back (45mm)	$900
(b)	As above, but with Swords (mit Schwertern)	1,000
(c)	Small red leather titled case	450

Nr. 155a

Nr. 155c

Nr. 155b

156. Order of the German Eagle, 5th Class 1943-5
(Deutsche Adlerorden Fünste Klasse)

(a)	Breast Cross (45mm) worn on ribbon.................................	$750
(b)	As above, but with Swords (mit Schwertern)....................	800
(c)	Small red leather titled case..	400

Nr. 156c

Nr. 156a

Nr. 156b, cased

157. The German Order 1942-45
(Deutscher Orden)

(a)	1st Class Neck Cross, wreathed swords design (Halskreuz)		*
(b)	2nd Class Neck Cross but without laurel leaves & swords (Halskreuz)	$15,000	
(c)	3rd Class Breast Cross, pin back (Steckkreuz)	10,000	
(d)	Red leather presentation cases	3,000	

**Only 10 presentation awards known 1942-45.

R. McCarthy

Nr. 157a

Dr. Klietmann

Nr. 157d

Dr. Klietmann

Dr. Klietmann

Dr. Klietmann

Nr. 157b

Dr. Klietmann

Dr. Klietmann

Nr. 157c

158. German National Prize for Art & Science 1937-45
(Ehrenzeichen des Deutsche Nationalpreises für Kunst und Wissenschaft)

(a)	Massive Breast Star, pin back in gold & platinum, inset with diamond brilliants...	*
(b)	Silk sash and rosette..	*
(c)	Large presentation Case...	*

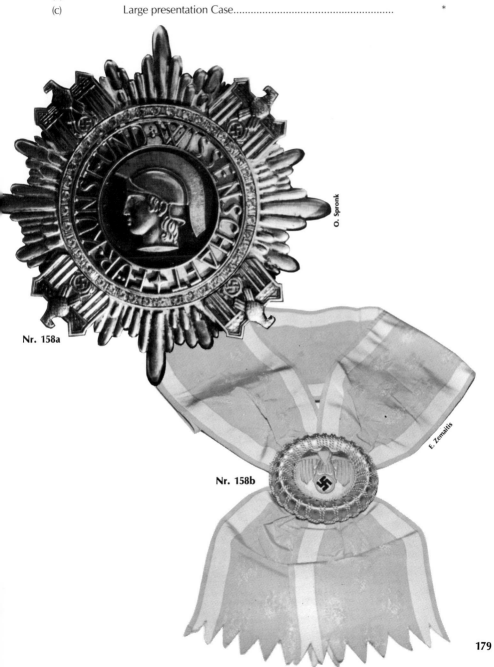

O. Spronk

Nr. 158a

Nr. 158b

E. Zemaitis

Nr. 158c, cased set

Jörg N. Hormann

159. German Red Cross Decorations 1934-37 (No Swastika)
(Ehrenzeichen des Deutschen Roten Kreuzes)

(a)	1st Class Neck Cross (53mm) (Erste Klasse).......................	$550
(b)	Breast Star (73mm) pin back (Stern)..................................	1,200
(c)	Cross of Merit, pin back (Verdienstkreuz)	200
(d)	Decoration of the Red Cross (40mm) on breast ribbon (Ehrenzeichen)...	100
(e)	Ladies' Cross (40mm) worn on ribbon bow (Damenkreuz)	100
(f)	Red leather titled cases...	75-150

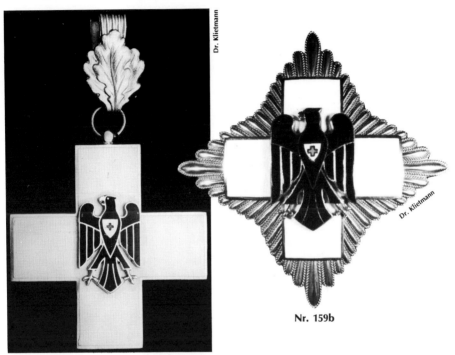

Nr. 159a

Nr. 159b

Nr. 159c

Nr. 159d

160. German Red Cross Decorations 1937-39(With Swastika) (Ehrenzeichen des Deutschen Roten Kreuzes)

(a)	Grand Cross Sash Badge (52mm) & Breast Star (84mm) (Grosskreuz)...	$5,000
(b)	Breast Star (84mm) (Stern)	3,000
(c)	1st Class Neck Cross with Oak Leaves (52mm) (Erste Stufe)......................................	1,500
(d)	Special Grade Neck Cross with Diamonds ("Sonderstufe",mit Brillanten)..	*
(e)	Cross of Merit (Verdienstkreuz)pin back	500
(f)	2nd Class Breast Cross (Zweite Klasse)worn on ribbon....	250
(g)	Womens Cross (Frauenkreuz)worn on ribbon bow	250
(h)	Enamelled Medal (Medaille)..	175
(i)	Red leatherette cases for all above classes of Decoration included in price	

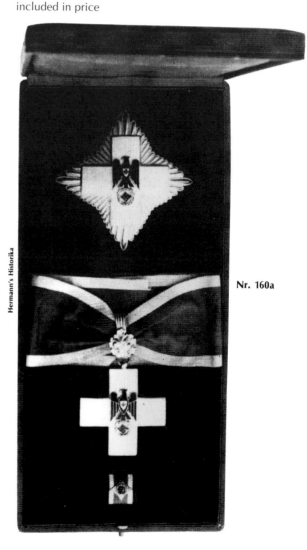

Hermann's Historika

Nr. 160a

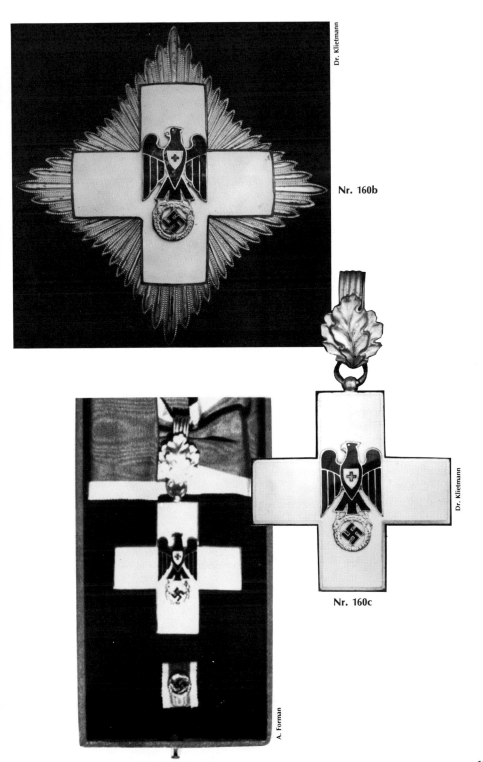

Dr. Klietmann

Nr. 160b

Dr. Klietmann

Nr. 160c

A. Forman

Nr. 160c cased

183

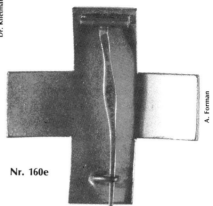

Dr. Klietmann

A. Forman

Nr. 160e

Dr. Klietmann

Nr. 160f

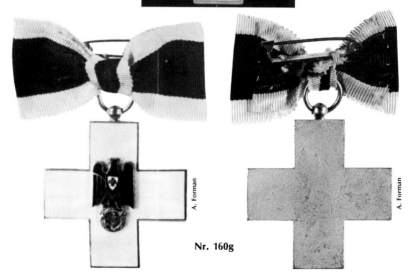

A. Forman

A. Forman

Nr. 160g

Nr. 160g with ribbon-bow

A. Forman

Below: Nr. 160i

A. Forman

A. Forman

Nr. 160h

Dr. Klietmann

A. Forman

161. D.R.K. Sisters Cross
(Das D.R.K. Schwesternkreuz)

(a)	Silver Cross for 10 years	$300
(b)	Silver Cross for 25 years	400
(c)	D.R.K. Long Service Cross for Matron (Oberin) (Gold)	500
(d)	D.R.K. Long Service Cross for Senior Matron (Gen. Oberin) (Gold)	750

Dr. Klietmann

Dr. Klietmann

Nr. 161a & b   **Nr. 161c & d**

A. Forman

Nr. 161 reverse and suspension chain

162. D.R.K. Pin of Honour
(Ehrennadel des D.R.K.)

(a)   Pin $250

Nr. 162

163. German Social Welfare Decorations 1939-45
(Ehrenzeichen für Deutsche Volkspflege)

(a)   Special Class Sash Badge (52mm) & Breast Star
(84mm) (Sonderstufe) .... *

Nr. 163

164. German Social Welfare Decorations
(Ehrenzeichen für Deutsche Volkspflege)

(a)   Special Class 1st Class Ladies Decoration with diamonds
(Sonderstufe mit Brillanten) .... *

(b)   Special presentation casket .... *

(Above awarded to ladies only on ribbon bow)

(c)	1st Class Neck Cross (52mm) (Erste Klasse)........................	$1,750
(d)	2nd Class Breast Cross pin back (Zweite Stufe)................	500
(e)	3rd Class Breast Cross on ribbon (Dritte Stufe)	200
(f)	Social Welfare Medal (Medaille)..	40
(g)	Red leatherette cases for all classes of decoration, except medal which has titled paper packet................................	100-400

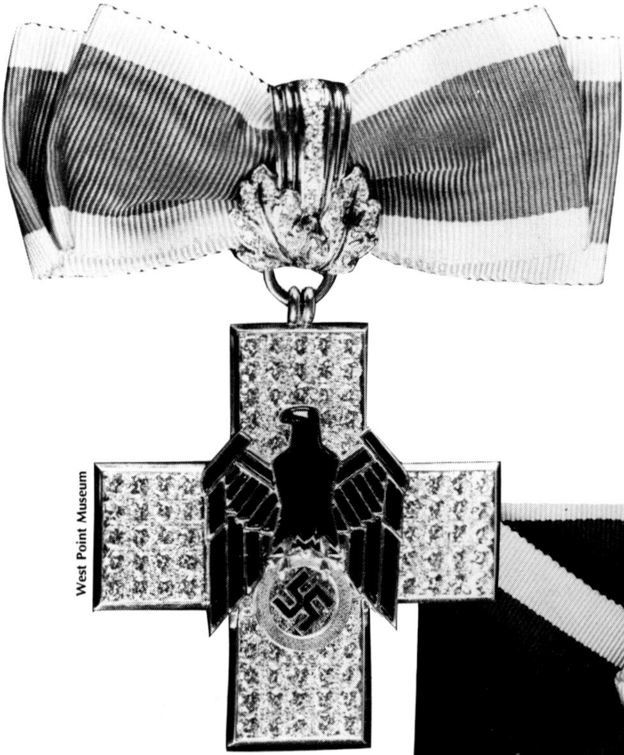

West Point Museum

Nr. 164a

Dr. Klietmann

Nr. 164c

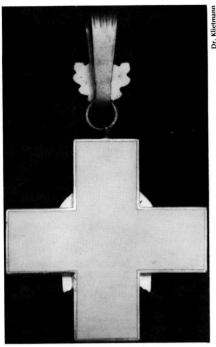

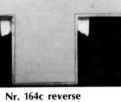

Nr. 164c reverse

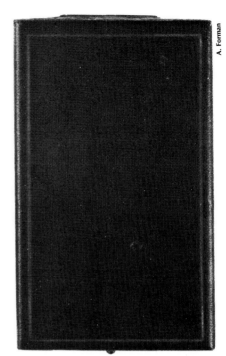

Nr. 164 case

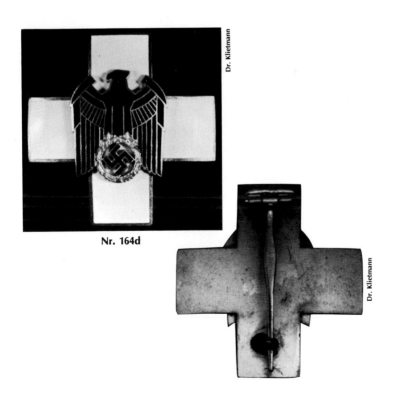

Nr. 164d

Dr. Klietmann

A. Forman

Nr. 164e

A. Forman

Nr. 164e cased

A. Forman

Dr. Klietmann

Dr. Klietmann

Nr. 164f

Dr. Klietmann

Nr. 164g, titled packet

165. German Olympic Games Decorations 1936 (Deutsches Olympiaehrenzeichen)

(a)   1st Class Neck Cross
  (Erste Stufe) (767 awarded)...................................... $2,000
(b)   2nd Class Breast Cross
  (Zweite Klasse) (3,364 awarded) 900
(c)   White leatherette cases for above decorations............ 250-500
  Note: Several manufacturers' variations exist.

Dr. Klietmann   Nr. 165a

Nr. 165c   A. Forman

Nr. 165b

166. Olympic Games Commemorative Medal 1936
(Olympia-Erinneurungsmedaille)

Nr. 166a

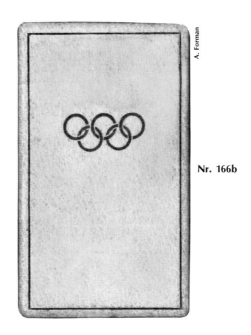

A. Forman

Nr. 166b

167. Civil Defence Decorations 1938
(Luftschutz Ehrenzeichen)

(a)	1st Class Cross (Erste Klasse,) in brass, alloy or zinc (Less than 150 awarded)	$600-750
(b)	Grey case	150
(c)	2nd Class Medal (Zweite Stufe)	40
(d)	Grey Carton or titled paper packet	75-100

Dr. Klietmann

Nr. 167a

Dr. Klietmann

Nr. 167c

A. Forman

Nr. 167d titled packet
and carton (below)

A. Forman

168. Fire Brigade Decorations 1936
(Feurwehr Ehrenzeichen)

(a)	1st Class Cross (60mm) 1936, pin back (Erste Stufe)..	$1,000
(b)	1st Class Cross (33mm) 1938, on breast ribbon (Erste Stufe)..	700
(c)	2nd Class Cross (33mm) on breast ribbon (Zweite Stufe)	175
(d)	Large titled paper packet for 1st Class 1936 (60mm)Cross	150
(e)	Black leatherette cases for other crosses	75-150

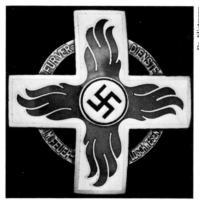 

Nr. 168a

Nr. 168b

Nr. 168e

196

Nr. 168c

169. Mine Rescue Service Decorations 1936
(Grubenwehr Ehrenzeichen)

(a)	Large pin back Medal 1936 (50mm).............................	$1,000
(b)	Black leatherette case..	150
(c)	Silver Medal 1938 (35mm)..	200

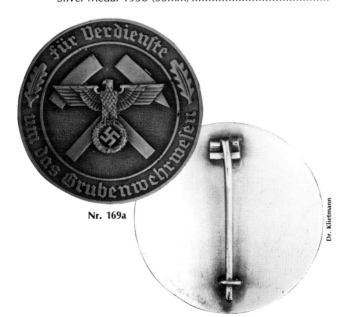

Nr. 169a

Nr. 169c

Dr. Klietmann

170. Cross of Honour of the German Mother 1938
(Ehrenzeichen der Deutschen Mutter)

(a) First Form 1st Class in Gold"Das Kind Adelt Die Mutter" 1938 ...	$1,200
(b) First Form 2nd Class in Silver"Das Kind Adelt Die Mutter" 1938	900
(c) First Form 3rd Class in Bronze"Das Kind Adelt Die Mutter" 1938	750
(d) 1st Class in Gold (16 December 1938)......................	50
(e) 2nd Class in Silver (16 December 1938)...................	40
(f) 3rd Class in Bronze (16 December 1938)...................	30
(g) Blue Case for 1st Class..	60
(h) Large titled paper packets for 2nd & 3rd Classes........	50

Dr. Klietmann

Nr. 170a, b & c,
First Form

Nr. 170d, e & f

Dr. Klietmann

171. German Life Saving Medal 1937 (Rettungsmedaille)

(a) Type A Official issue by Prussian State Mint
in "800" Hallmarked silver (Silber)............................. $400
(b) Type B Private purchase silver-plated brass or zinc............... 150
(c)   Black leatherette case... 100

Dr. Klietmann

Nr. 171a & b

Nr. 170a
on ribbon

A. Forman

172. German Life Saving Medallion 1937
(Erinneurungs Medaille für Rettung aus Gefahr)

(a)   Fine quality silver striking(48mm)............................ $400
                        Prussian State Mint in "835" Hallmarked silver
(b)   Black leatherette case..   100

Nr. 172a

173. Eagle Shield of Germany 1934
(Adlerschild des Deutschen Reiches)

(a)   Large bronze medallion (110mm)...................................   *
(b)   Large case..   *

Nr. 173a

174. Goethe Medal for Art & Science 1933
(Goethe Medaille für Kunst und Wissenschaft)

(a)	Large silver medallion (71mm)..	$5,000
(b)	Black case..	*

**Awarded pieces named on rim. Although un-named specimens are known, these would be about 50% of catalogue value.

Nr. 174a

Dr. Klietmann

E. Zemaitis

Nr. 174b

E. Zemaitis

175. Badge of Honour for Members of the National Senate of Culture 1936
(Ehrenplakette für die Mitglieder des Reichskultursenate)

(a) Type A   Badge hallmarked "900" silver-gilt enamel. Reverse solid-ball rivets, by "Deschler" of Munich. Engraved issue number. Only 125 awarded in 1936 .... $7,500

       Type B   Badge hallmarked, "900" silver gilt & enamel. Reverse hollow-rivets by "Deschler" of Munich. Engraved issue number. About 200-250 awarded $6,500

(b)   Deluxe Red Case .... *

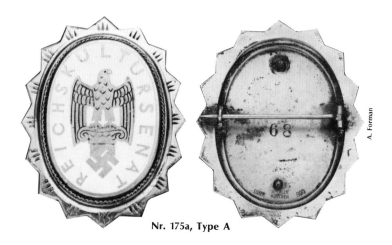

Nr. 175a, Type A

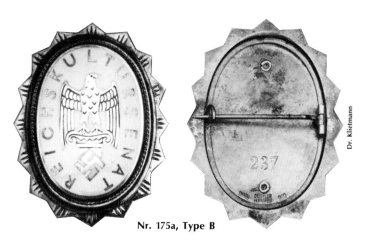

Nr. 175a, Type B

176. German Academy for Aeronautical Research Membership Badges 1938
(Die Deutsche Akademie der Luftfahrforschung)

(a)	President & Presidium members chain of office (Amtskette) hallmarked silver-gilt	$25,000
(b)	Gold Badge for Honourary Members (57mm)	5,000
(c)	Miniature Gold Badge	1,500
(d)	Silver Badge for Sponsoring Members (Forderden Mitgliedern) (57mm) (Only one awarded)	*
(e)	Miniature Silver Badge	*

**Two forms of suspender, fixed and loop.

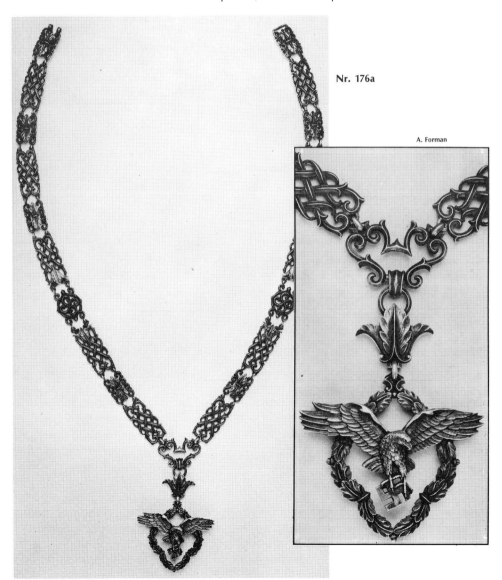

Nr. 176a

A. Forman

A. Forman

Nr. 176b

(f)	Bronze Badge for Corresponding Members (Korrespondierenden Mitgliedern) (57mm)	2,500
(g)	Miniature Bronze Badge	1,000
(h)	Black leatherette case for badges (57mm)	500

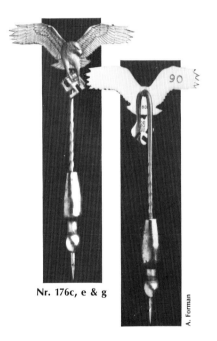

Nr. 176c, e & g

A. Forman

S. Wolfe

Nr. 176b with fixed suspender

177. Hermann Göring Commemorative Medaillon 1939 (Hermann Göring-Denkmünze)

**This unique award was seen by the author in an edition of Luftwehr 1939. Conferred by Göring as President of the Adademy to Prof. Dr. Prandtl (as "Chef der Luftwehr"), at a ceremony. Described in text as the highest award of the academy, it was almost certainly in gold (75mm).

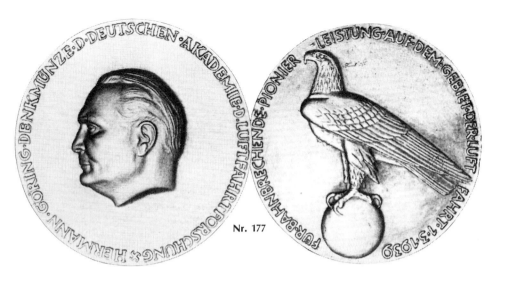

Nr. 177

178. "Pioneer of Labour" Decoration 1940 (Ehrenzeichen "Pioneer der Arbeit")

(a)   Presentation award decoration hallmarked "900" silver-gilt and enamel. Reverse, two rivets. Pinback........................   *

(b)   Presentation deluxe large red leather case. Gold emblem on lid *

(c)   Presentation miniature award, hallmarked "900" & enamel, reverse riveted. Silver-gilt needle pin................   *

(d)   Presentation deluxe red leather case. Gold emblem on lid   *

**Only eighteen presentation award decorations, awarded with matching cased miniatures and deluxe large folder/presentation documents. In recent years, only one cased set of decoration, miniature and document have surfaced (issue Nr 16).

A. Forman

Nr. 178a

A. Forman

Nr. 178b

Nr. 178c

A. Forman

Hermann's Historika

DER FÜHRER

Selbstlos in seinem Einsatz, unermüdlich
in der Planung und Durchführung neuer
Geräte und Methoden, hervorragend in
seinem handwerklichen und konstruktiven
Können und seinen Mitarbeitern jederzeit
ein wahrer Kamerad ist der

Uhrmachermeister
Parteigenosse John Schwarzer

dem ich heute am Nationalfeiertag
des Deutschen Volkes auf Vorschlag des
Reichsorganisationsleiters und Leiters der
Deutschen Arbeitsfront als sechzehntem
Schaffenden die Auszeichnung

PIONIER DER ARBEIT
und das Ehrenzeichen
hierzu in Gold verleihe

Berlin, den 1. Mai 1944

**Above: Nr. 176a cased,
presentation document
and cased miniature**

A. Forman

179. Badge of Honour of the Dr. Fritz Todt Prize
(Ehrennadel des Dr Fritz Todt Preises)

(a) Type A   1st pattern actual award badges, titled, "DR. ING. FRITZ TODT PREIS' reverse with date, "8. 2. 44". And impressed issue number, all Badges struck in Aluminum (Lightweight).

(b)   1st Class in Gold (Erste Stufe) ....   *

(c)   2nd Class in Silver (Zweite Stufe) $3,000

(d)   3rd Class in Steel (Dritte Stufe)   2,000

(e)   Presentation cases ....   *

**From the 1st Presentation ceremony in late 1944, this author has located only one Gold Prize Award (Issue Nr 5). It is doubtful if more than a handful were awarded due to the size of the cash prize accompanying the awards plus the crucial war situation in late 1944/early 1945.

Nr. 179b,
Type A

Nr. 179d reverse

Nr. 179b reverse

(f) Type B   2nd pattern badges titled, 'DR. FRITZ TODT'. Private purchase badges plain grained reverse.

(g)   1st Class in Gold (Erste Stufe) $900

(h)   2nd Class in Silver (Zweite Stufe) 500

(i)   3rd Class in Steel (Dritte Stufe) 400

(j) Type C   Variation title, 'DR. ING. FRITZ TODT PREIS'. Private purchase badges plain on reverse.

(k)   1st Class in Gold (Erste Stufe) $1,500

(l)   2nd Class in Silver (Zweite Stufe) 800

(m)   3rd Class in Steel (Dritte Stufe) 500

         Above examples of Type B & Type C usually found on manufacturers' sample boards or loose from tailor shops.

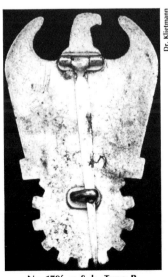

Nr. 179f, g & h, Type B

180. "Defence Economy Leader" Decoration 1939 (Ehrenzeichen "Wehrwirtschaftsführer")

(a)   Gilt bronze or gilt alloy pin back $500

(b)   Miniature half size stick pin badge 200

Nr. 180a

Nr. 180b

181. Silver Clasp for Female S.S. Auxiliaries 1943 (Silberspange der S.S. Helferinnen)

(a)   Hallmarked "800" silver, pin back (Silber) $3,000

Nr. 181a

Nr. 181a, reverse, enlarged   Dr. Klietmann

182. S.S. Long Service Awards 1938
(S.S. Dienstauzeichnungen)

(a)	Black medal for 4 years	$200
(b)	Black carton (white S.S. Sigrunes)	150
(c)	Bronze medal for 8 years	300
(d)	Black carton (silver S.S. Sigrunes)	200
(e)	Silver Cross (swastika) for 12 years	1,000
(f)	Black deluxe case (silver S.S. Sigrunes)	300
(g)	Gold Cross (swastika) for 25 years	1,500
(h)	Black deluxe case (gold S.S. Sigrunes)	500

The wide ribbon for 12 & 25 year crosses, with S.S. Sigrune silver or gold wire emblem, is extremely rare, above prices include this ribbon. Crosses without ribbon are worth 25% less.

Dr. Klietmann

Nr. 182a

A. Forman

Nr. 182b

Nr. 182c

Nr. 182f & g

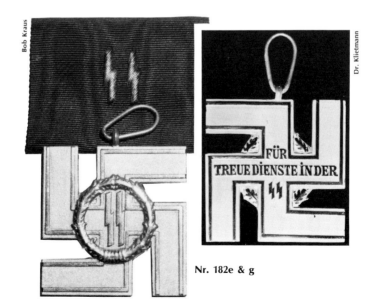

Nr. 182e & g

Note: First form crosses have ring suspenders, not loops.

Nr. 182f & g

A. Forman

Nr. 182b

Nr. 182d

Nr. 182f & h

213

183. Faithful Service Decorations 1938
(Treudienst Ehrenzeichen)

(a)	Special Class for 50 years (Sonderstufe)	$250
(b)	Red case with gold "50"	75
(c)	1st Class in Gold for 40 years (Erste Stufe)	65
(d)	Red case with gold "40"	30
(e)	2nd Class in Silver for 25 years (Zweite Stufe)	45
(f)	Red carton with silver "25" within Cog	20

Dr. Klietmann

Nr. 183a

A. Forman

Nr. 183b

Nr. 183c & e

Dr. Klietmann

A. Forman

Nr. 183f

Nr. 183f, but
in case form

Nr. 183d

215

184. Police Expert Skier Badge 1942
(Polizei Schiführerabzeichen)

Badge in grey aluminum, pin back.. $1,000

Nr. 184

185. Police Expert Alpine Badge 1936
(Gendarmerie Alpine Abzeichen)

Badge of Austrian manufacture and style of attachment on reverse, Silvered brass & enamel with maker's mark.. $1,250

Nr. 185

186. Police Expert High Alpine Badge 1936
(Gendarmerie Hoch-Alpinistabzeichen)

Badge of Austrian manufacture and style of attachment on reverse, silvered brass & enamel with maker's mark.......................... $1,500

216

187. Police Bergführer Badge 1941
(Polizei-Bergführer der Ordnungspolizei)

Badge silvered brass and enamel, pin back.. $1,500

Nr. 187

188. Police Long Service Awards 1938
(Polizei Dienstauszeichnungen)

(a)	1st Class in Gold for 25 years..	$225
(b)	Green deluxe case with gold "25" wreathed...................	85
(c)	2nd Class in Silver for 18 years...	175
(d)	Green deluxe case with silver "18" wreathed.................	75
(e)	Silver medal for 8 years	90
(f)	Green carton with silver "8" wreathed............................	60

Nr. 188a

Nr. 188b

Nr. 188d

Dr. Klietmann

Nr. 188c

Nr. 188e

189. Customs Service Decoration 1939
(Zollgrenzschutz-Ehrenzeichen)

(a)   Cross in bronze or alloy $200

(b)   Green deluxe case or LDO carton..................................... 50-100

    **The wide ribbon with yellow wreathed eagle emblem is very rare.
Without ribbon value at least 40% less.

Nr. 189a

219

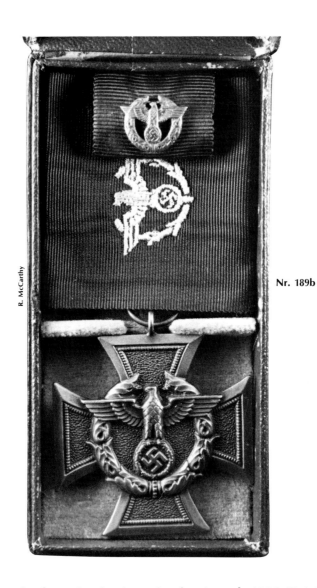

R. McCarthy

190. National Labour Service Long Service Awards 1938 (R.A.D.)
(Dienstauszeichnungen für den Reichsarbeitsdienst)

	Type A	First design as awarded to male personnel	
(a)		1st Class Medal in Gold for 25 years with eagle emblem on ribbon..	$300
(b)		Olive-brown case with gold "25" within cog....................	150
(c)		2nd Class Silver Medal for 18 years with eagle emblem on ribbon..	175
(d)		Olive-brown case with silver "18" within cog..................	100
(e)		3rd Class Silver Medal for 12 years....................................	125
(f)		Olive-brown carton with silver "12" within cog	75
(g)		4th Class Bronze Medal for 4 years....................................	50
(h)		Olive-brown carton with silver "4" within cog	50

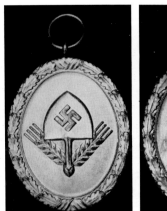

Nrs. 190a, c, e & g, Type A

	Type B	Second design as awarded to female personnel, worn on ribbon bow.	
(a)		1st Class Medal in Gold for 25 years with eagle emblem on ribbon...	$400
(b)		Olive-brown case with gold "25" within wreath..............	150
(c)		2nd Class Silver Medal for 18 years with eagle emblem on ribbon...	300
(d)		Olive-brown case with silver "18" within wreath.............	100
(e)		3rd Class Silver Medal for 12 years	200
(f)		Olive-brown carton with silver "12" within wreath	100
(g)		4th Class Bronze Medal for 4 years.....................................	150
(h)		Olive-brown carton with silver "4" within cog	75

Nrs. 190a, c, e & g, Type B

221

191. N.S.D.A.P. Long Service Awards
(Dienstauszeichnungen der N.S.D.A.P.)

(a)	Cross for 25 years, gilt and enamel	$1,200
(b)	Red deluxe case	250
(c)	Cross for 15 years, silver and enamel	250
(d)	Blue carton	100
(e)	Cross for 10 years.Bronze, aliminum or zinc	150
(f)	Brown carton	75

Dr. Klietmann

Nr. 191a

A. Forman

Nr. 191b

Dr. Klietmann

Nr. 191c

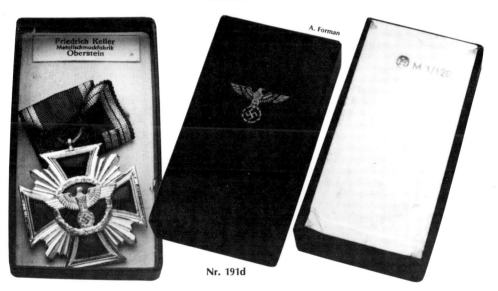

Friedrich Keller
Metallschmuckfabrik
Oberstein

A. Forman

M 1/120

Nr. 191d

Dr. Klietmann

Nr. 191e

192. N.S.D.A.P. Golden Party Badge
(Goldenes Parteiabzeichen)

Type A   Gold-plated & enamel. Issue numbered on reverse.
Some maker marked.

(a)   25mm size (civilian dress)... $350

(b)   30mm size (N.S.D.A.P. uniform).................................... 600

Nr. 192a, Type A

Nr. 192b, Type A

Type B   Official Adolf Hitler presentation awards. Impressed or
engraved on reverse with date of award. "30th January &
year". Also "A.H."

(c)   25mm size... $2,000

(d)   30mm size... 3,000

(e)   Matched set with indentical date & year......................... 6,000

(f)   Deluxe red leather dual-award case for 30mm & 25mm
presentation set.. 1,000

Nr. 192d, Type B

S. Wolfe

30.1.1943
A.H.

Nr. 192c,
Type B

GES.GESCH

A.H.
30.1.1939

A. Forman

Nr. 192d, Type B

Nr. 192e

S. Wolfe

DE SCHLER
MÜNCHEN 2

A.H.
30.1.1938

Nr. 192c, Type B

GES.GESCH

A.H.
30.1.1938

S. Wolfe

Nr. 192d, Type B

225

193. Special N.S.D.A.P. Party Badge in Gold - Awarded by the Führer, to Foreigners
(Das Parteiabzeichen der NSDAP in Gold für Ausländer)

**Adolf Hitler is known to have presented such awards to several foreign, non-N.S.D.A.P. members as a visable sign of his personal favour. Dr. Klietmann refers to several known examples of this rare award! Col. M. Dodkins referred to an award to Admiral Horthy, Premier of Hungary in Littlejohn & Dodkins' 1st edition, 1968.

(a)   Deluxe quality solid silver, gold & enamel - bearing engraved signature of "Adolf Hitler". Deluxe pin fitting. $5,000

Nr. 193a

194. N.S.D.A.P.-"Blood Order" 1923-1933
(Blutorden)

(a)	Type A	First striking in hallmarked "800" silver by Fuess of Munich with buttonhole silk ribbon............	$3,000-3,500
(b)		Brown titled case	750
(c)	Type B	Second striking in "800" hallmarked silver without a makers mark and plain silk ribbon	1,500-2,000
(d)		Large plain red case..	400

Nr. 194a, Type A

226

Dr. Klietmann

Nr. 194c, Type B

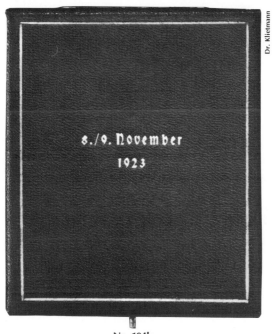

Dr. Klietmann

8./9. November
1923

Nr. 194b

Graf Ulrich wears the "Blood Order" in its traditional form.

Sister Pia, standing in the center, was the only female awarded the "Blood Order" by Hitler, November 9, 1936.

195. Gau Munich Commemorative Badge 9th November 1923-33 (Gau Munchen Erinnerungsabzeichen der 9. Nov. 1923)

(a)   Badge struck in bronze. Pin back................................. $150

Nr. 195a

196. The Coburg Badge 1936 (Coburger Abzeichen)

(a)   Type A   Badge in bronze. RZM marked, pin back $3,000

(b)   Case..   400

(c)   Type B   Unique example has been recorded in silver with red enamel swastika   4,000

(d)   Miniature bronze badge   500

Nr. 196

Heinrich Bennecke

197. Nuremburg Badge of Honour 1929
(Nürnberger Parteitagsabzeichen)

(a)   Variations exist in grey, silver or gilt metal in
             solid & hollow back form.. $175-250

Nr. 197a

Dr. Klietmann

E. Zemaitis

198. Nuremburg Badge of Honour 1929 - Non-Portable Award
(Nürnberger Parteitabsabzeichen)

(a)   Fine quality bronze, silver or gold-plated plaque
             in deluxe leather titled case.. $300-500

Nr. 198a

Bob Kraus

199. S.A. Ralley at Brunswick 1931 Badge of Honour
(Abzeichen des S.A. Treffens Braunschweig 1931)

(a)	Type A	First pattern, large badge, hollow back..............................	$250
(b)	Type B	Variations exist in tin and aluminum.................................	100

Nr. 199a, Type A   Nr. 199b, Type B

200. The "Frontbann" Badge 1924
(Frontbann-Abzeichen)

(a)	Oxidised silver badge, pin back..	$1,000
(b)	Miniature in silver..	300

Nr. 200a

201. N.S.D.A.P. Party District Commemorative Badges 1933
(Traditions-Gau Abzeichen)

(a)	Type A	With either dates 1923 or 1925. Fine quality "800" hallmarked silver & enamel. With maker's mark.............	$2,000
(b)	Type B	With either dates 1923 or 1925, fine quality "800" hallmarked silver & black paint finish. With maker's mark	1,500
(c)		Miniature in silver & enamel...	500

202. Gau Berlin 1936

(a)	Type A	Fine quality gold-plated & enamel with maker's mark and issue number (only 30 awards)..........................	$6,000
(b)	Type B	Fine quality silver plated & enamel with maker's mark and issue number..	4,000
(c)		Case..	750-1,000
(d)		Miniature in bronze & enamel..	1000

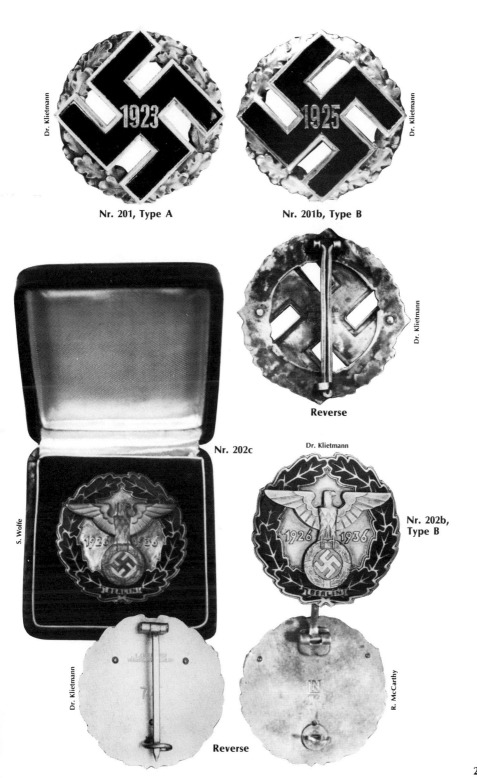

Nr. 201, Type A

Nr. 201b, Type B

Dr. Klietmann

Dr. Klietmann

Reverse

Nr. 202c

S. Wolfe

Dr. Klietmann

Nr. 202b,
Type B

Dr. Klietmann

R. McCarthy

Reverse

233

Heinrich Georg
Graf Finck von
Finckenstein wears
the Nuremberg
Badge of Honor
(Nr. 199).

The Party official above wears the Party District Commemorative Badge (Nr. 201).

Tim Knight

Amtsleiter Emil Behrendt. Note positioning of the "Frontbann" Badge (Nr. 200).

203. Gau Baden

(a)	Type A	Large oval, gold-plated with maker's mark	$2,500
(b)	Type B	Large oval, silver-plated with maker's mark.......................	1,500
(c)	Type C	Small round silver-plated badge, possibly for award to women..	1,250
(d)		Case..	300
(e)		Miniature in silver...	300

Dr. Klietmann

Nr. 203a & b

R. McCarthy

Nr. 203c

204. Gau Thuringen 1936
(Gauabzeichen für Thüringer)

(a)	Type A	Badge fine quality "800" hallmarked silver, and issue numbered..	$2,500
(b)	Type B	Badge fine quality bronze striking. Issue numbered........	2,000
(c)		Case..	400
(d)		Miniature in silver...	400

205. East Hanover Gau Commemorative Badge 1933
(Traditionsabzeichen des Gaues Osthannover der N.S.D.A.P.)

(a)		Gold Class Badge..	$2,500
(b)		Silver Class Badge..	1,500
(c)		Bronze Class Badge	1,000
(d)		Miniature..	100-250

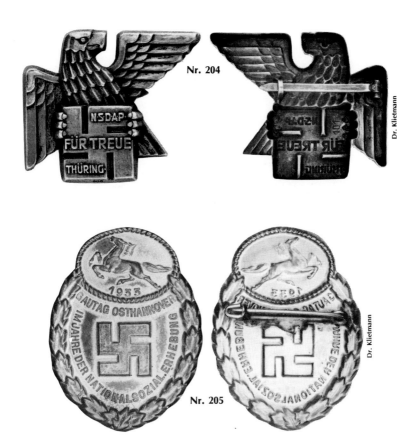

Nr. 204

Dr. Klietmann

Nr. 205

Dr. Klietmann

206. Gau Danzig Commemorative Badge 1939
(Gau Traditionsabzeichen des Gaues Danzig Westpreussen)

(a)   There are several variation badges in hallmarked silver
and in aliminium $2,000-3,500

(b)   Miniature in silver 500-1,000

Nr. 206a

Dr. Klietmann

207. Gau East Prussian Commemorative Badge 1938
(Gau-Ehrenzeichen des Gaues Ostpreussen)

(a)   Variations exist in silver-plated metal with maker's
        mark and silvered alloy $2,500-3,000
(b)   Miniature   500

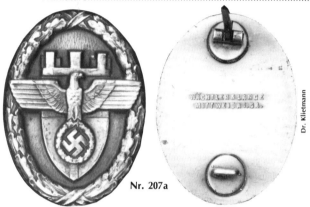

Nr. 207a

Dr. Klietmann

208. Gau Essen Commemorative Badge 1935
(Gau-Traditionabzeichen Essen)

(a)   Special Gold Class. Only four awarded. In solid gold. ...... *
(b)   Gold Class Badge. Gold-plated bronze.
        Size: 41mm X 20mm $3,000
(c)   Silver Class Badge. Hallmarked "935" silver.
        Size: 41mm X 20mm $2,500
**In 1935 Adolf Hitler, Hermann Goring, and Dr. Robert Ley each recieved
a solid gold badge. In 1939 Gauleiter Heinrich Unger (Essen) also received
such a badge. The award badge is much rarer than previously indicated.
Both its size and appearance is different from the larger and very common
aluminum rally badges.

 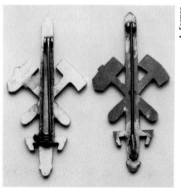

A. Forman

A. Forman

Nr. 208b & c

209. Gau Sudentenland Commemorative Badge 1938
(Gau-Ehrenzeichen des Gaues Sudentenland der N.S.D.A.P.)

(a)   Variations exist in both brass and deluxe hallmarked
silver and enamel... $3,000-3,500

(b)   Case.. 400

(c)   Miniature... 1000

Nr. 209

210. Gau Warthe Commemorative Badge 1939
(Gau Wartheland-Traditionsabzeichen)

(a)   Fine quality riveted, silver-gilt and enamel.
Issue numbered.. $4,000

(b)   Large Miniature lapel pin, fine quality plated metal........ 1,000

(c)   Case.. 500

Nr. 210a

Dr. Klietmann

R. McCarthy

239

211. H.J. Potsdam Badge 1932
(Potsdam-Abzeichen)

(a)   Fine quality silver badge $200

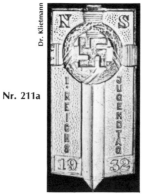

Nr. 211a

212. Anhalt Labour Service Commemorative Badge 1932
(Anhalt Arbeitsdienst Erinnerungsabzeichen)

There are two versions of the badge, one bearing the the date 1932 and the other without a date.

(a)   Gold Class Badge.. $750
(b)   Silver Class Badge..   500
(c)   Steel Class Badge - grey metal..   400

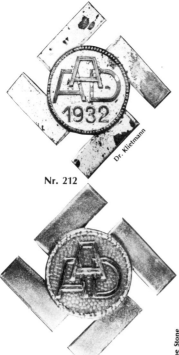

Nr. 212

213. Decoration of the Technical Emergency Service 1935
(Ehrenzeichen der Technishen Nothilfe)

(a)   Awarded with the following dates;
          1919, 1920, 1921, 1922, 1923 .... $500
(b)   Deluxe black case 150

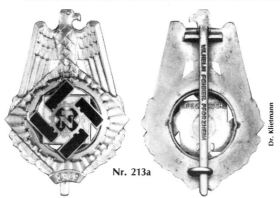

Nr. 213a

214. "Stahlhelm" Commemorative Badges 1933
(Traditionsabzeichen des "Stahlhelm")

Awarded with the following dates:

(a)	"1918"	$750
(b)	"1919"	200
(c)	"1920"	200
(d)	"1921"	100
(e)	"1922"	75
(f)	"1923"	75
(g)	"1924"	75
(h)	"1925"	75
(i)	"1926"	75
(j)	"1927"	75
(k)	"1928"	100
(l)	"1929"	75
(m)	"1930"	75
(n)	"1931"	75
(o)	"1932"	75

Nr. 214l   Nr. 214n, reverse

215. "Stahlhelm" Award Badges 1933

(a)		Wehrsportkreuz, quality plated metal and enamel	$750
(b)		Deluxe green case...	150

Nr. 215a

216. Danzig Cross 1939
(Danziger Kreuz)

(a)		1st Class Cross (Only 88 awarded).......................................	$1,000
(b)		Deluxe red "Danzig" case...	350
(c)		2nd Class Cross (Only 254 awarded)	600
(d)		Deluxe red "Danzig" case...	250

 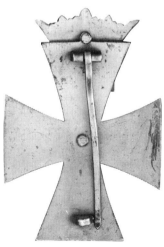

Nr. 216a

Nr. 216c

Reinhard Heydrich
wears Nr. 216a.

Dr. Klietmann

217. Danzig Life Saving Medal
(Rettungsmedaille)

(a)   Medal is oxidised silver, hallmarked "900 " $1,200

Nr. 217

218. Danzig Fire Brigade Decoration 1939
(Feurwehr-Ehrenzeichen)

(a)   1st Class Cross, gold-plated & enamel............................... $1,000
(b)   2nd Class Cross in silver & enamel..................................... 750

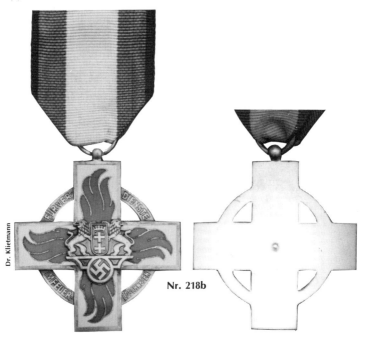

Nr. 218b

219. Danzig Faithful Service Decoration 1938
(Treuedienst Ehrenzeichen)

(a)	Special Class Gold Cross for 50 years. Gold-plated with "50"..	$1,000
(b)	1st Class Gold Cross for 40 years. Gold-plated...................	700
(c)	2nd Class Silver Cross for 25 years......................................	550

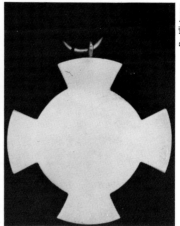

Nr. 219b & c

220. Danzig Police Long Service Awards 1938
(Polizei-Dienstauszeichnungen)

(a)	1st Class Gold Cross for 25 years..	$900
(b)	2nd Class Silver Cross for 18 years..	600
(c)	Silver Medal for 8 years	500

Nr. 220a & b

Nr. 220c

221. Danzig Red Cross Decorations
(Ehrenzeichen des Roten Kreuzes)

(a)	Decoration of Merit	$1,000
(b)	Cross of Merit 1st Class for 25 years, pin back	750
(c)	Cross of Merit 2nd Class for 10 years	600

Nr. 221a

Nr. 221b

Nr. 221c

222. Danzig Flak Battle Badge of the City
(Flakkampfabzeichen der Stadt Danzig)

(a)   Fine quality silver striking.. $1,800

Nr. 222

223. N.S.F.K. Badge for Powered Aircraft Pilot (1st Design) 1938 (Abzeichen für Motorflugzeugführer)

(a)	Fine quality silver bullion on cloth backing, in patch form	$1,500
(b)	(2nd Design) 1942. Struck in silver-plated brass, numbered on reverse	2,200
(c)	Titled deluxe black case	500

Dr. Klietmann

George Petersen

Nr. 223a

Nr. 223b

A. Southard

NSFK

MOTORFLUGZEUGF. ABZ.

Nr. 223c

224. N.S.F.K. Badge for Powered Aircraft Pilot (3rd Design) 1943
(Abzeichen für Motorflugzeugführer)

(a)	Badge struck in grey metal, numbered on reverse..........	$2,500
(b)	Titled deluxe black case...	500

Nr. 224a

225. N.S.F.K. Badge for Free Balloon Pilot (1st Design) 1938
(Abzeichen für Freiballonführer)

(a)	Fine quality silver bullion on cloth backing in patch form..	$1,000

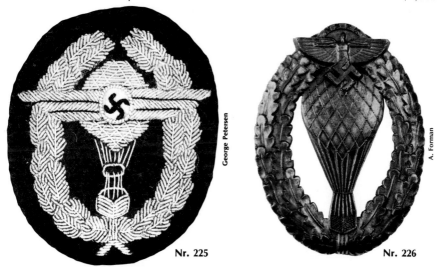

Nr. 225

Nr. 226

226. N.S.F.K. Badge for Free Ballon Pilot (2nd Design) c. 1943
(Abzeichen für Freiballonführer)

(a)	Silver grey metal, numbered on reverse	$2,500
(b)	Titled deluxe black case...	500

227. N.S.F.K. Large Glider Pilots Badge 1942 (Grosses Segelflieger-Abzeichen)

(a)	Silver-plated metal & enamel. Reverse serial-numbered	$1,500
(b)	Titled deluxe black case...	400

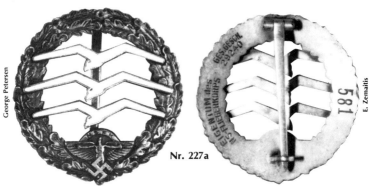

Nr. 227a

228. N.S.F.K. Aero-Modeling Proficiency Badges (N.S.F.K. Modell-Flugleistungsabzeichen)

Awards in both cloth patch form, or metal pin back badges. Also lapel badges.

(a)	Grade A round badge	$750
(b)	Grade B round badge..	500
(c)	Grade C round badge..	400
(d)	Large Miniature Lapel Badges in Metal. Stick-pin form..	$50-100

Nr. 228a

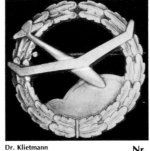

Dr. Klietmann

Nr. 228c

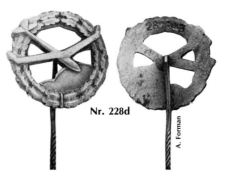

Nr. 228d

250

229. S.A. Military Sports Badge
   ### (S.A. Wehrabzeichen)

(a)	1st Class in Gold		$175
(b)	2nd Class in Silver		125
(c)	3rd Class in Bronze		50

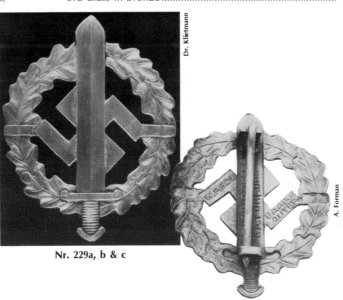

Nr. 229a, b & c

230. S.A. Military Sports Badge for War Wounded 1943
   ### (S.A. Wehrabzeichen für Kreigsversehrte)

(a)	Badges usually Bronzed alloy or zinc		$300

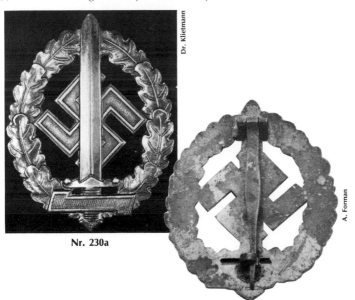

Nr. 230a

231. D.R.A. Sports Badges c.1933
(Deutsches Reichsabzeichen für Leibesübungen)

First design without Swastika

(a)	1st Class in Gold	$100
(b)	2nd Class in Silver	60
(c)	3rd Class in Bronze	30

Nr. 231

232. D.R.L. Sports Badge pre-1937
(Deutsches Reichsabzeichen für Leibesübungen)

Second design without Swastika

(a)	1st Class in Gold	$100
(b)	2nd Class in Silver	60
(c)	3rd Class in Bronze	30

Nr. 232

233. D.R.L. Sports Badge 1937
(Deutsches Reichsabzeichen für Leibesübungen)

Third design with Swastika

(a)	1st Class in Gold	$150
(b)	2nd Class in Silver	75
(c)	3rd Class in Bronze	40

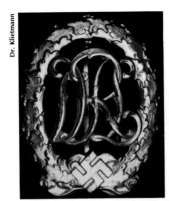
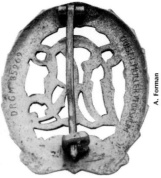

Nr. 233

**234. D.R.L. Sports Badge for the War Disabled 1942
(Versehrtensport-Abzeichen)**

(a)　　　　Badge (Silver with gold wreath) $200

**235. Achievement & Championship Badges of the N.S.R.L. & D.R.L.
(Leistungsabzeichen und Meisterschaftsabzeichen des
N.S.R.L. und D.R.L.)**

Lapel badges:

(a)	Achievement badge in bronze with date.........................	$100
(b)	Achievement badge in bronze without date..................	150
(c)	Achievement badge in silver with date............................	150
(d)	Achievement badge in silver without date......................	150
(e)	Champion badge in gold..	250

Nr. 235a & c　　　　**Nr. 235b & d**

253

236. Athletes Weight-Lifting Sports Badge
(Deutsches Schwerathleitikabzeichen)

(a)	Bronze Class	$450
(b)	Silver Class	750
(c)	Gold Class	900

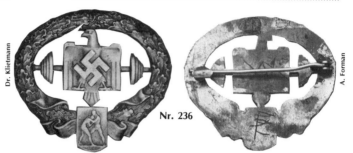

Nr. 236

237. S.A. German Expert Horsemans Badge 1937
(Deutsche Reiterführer-Abzeichen)

(a)   Fine quality oxidised silver badge. In silver or alloy with makers mark and issue number.

Pin back, variant fittings $2,500

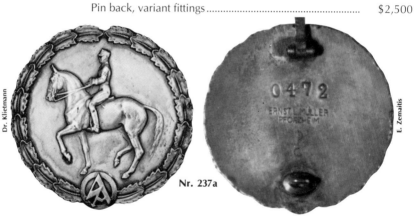

Nr. 237a

238. German Horsemans Sports Badge
(Deutsches Reiterabzeichen)

(a)	1st Class in Gold	$150
(b)	2nd Class in Silver	100
(c)	3rd Class in Bronze	75

239. German Horse Drivers Badge
(Deutsches Fahrer-Abzeichen)

(a)	1st Class in Gold	$200
(b)	2nd Class in Silver	150
(c)	3rd Class in Bronze	100

Dr. Klietmann

A. Forman

Nr. 238

Nr. 239

E. Zemaitis

Pre-1934 type

240. Badge for the Care of Horses 1937
(Deutsches Pferdepflegerabzeichen)

(a)	Grade I in Gold	$200
(b)	Grade II in Silver	150
(c)	Grade III in Bronze	125

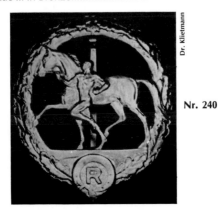

Dr. Klietmann

Nr. 240

241. German Young Horsemans Sports Badge
(Deutsches Jugend-Reiterabzeichen)

(a) Badge. In bronze or bronzed alloy $125

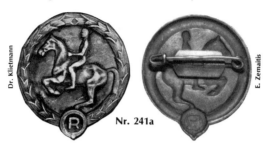

Nr. 241a

242. N.S.R.K. Plaque for Donations of Horses 1937
(Plakette für Zurverfügungstellung von Pferdern, u.s.w.)

(a) Plaque in blackened iron $150
(b) Large black case 75

Nr. 242a

243. German Motor Sports Badge 1939
(Deutsches Motorsportabzeichen)

(a)	1st Class in Gold. (Only 91 awarded)		$4,000
(b)	2nd Class in Silver. (Only 93 awarded)		3,000
(c)	3rd Class in Iron. (Only 314 awarded)		2,000
(d)	Deluxe cases		500

Nr. 243

Dr. Klietmann

244. Germanic Proficiency Runes Sport Badge 1943
(Germanische Leistungsrune)

Olive-bronzed zinc, silver-washed zinc or silver-plated metal. Reverse prongs to attach SS Sigrunes.

(a)	Silver Grade Badge		$1,800
(b)	Bronze Grade Badge		1,500

Dr. Klietmann

Nr. 244

257

245. National Sports Leaders Medallion "For an Outstanding Achievement" 1933
(Reichsssportführer Medailles "Im Anerkennung Einer Herragenden Leistung")

(a)	Medallion, struck in bronze	....	$250
(b)	Case	....	75

Nr. 245a

Nr. 245b

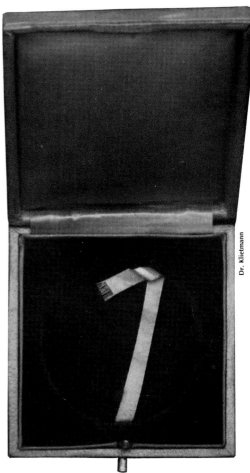

246. National Youth Sports Badge
(Reichsjugend Sportsabzeichen)

(a)   R.J.A. silver lapel badge. Types with & without Swastika $50

(b)   R.J.A. silver brooch for females..   100

Nr. 246a

247. H.J. Golden Leaders Sports Badge 1937
(Goldenes Führer-Sportsabzeichen)

(a)   Badges, Type A or B.. $300

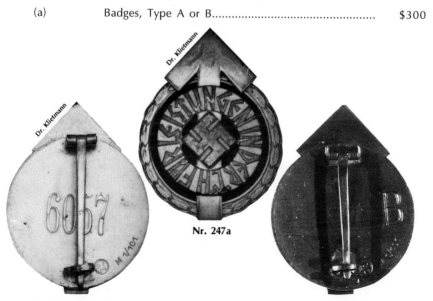

Nr. 247a

Nr. 247a, Type A   Nr. 247a, Type B

A. Southard

260   This Hitler Youth Leader wears the Golden Leader's Sports Badge (Nr. 247).

Oberst Niemack and members of Panzer-Grenadier-Division "Grossdeutschland" visit a Hitler Youth shooting range where youngsters are attempting to quality.

248. German Youth Champions Badge of Honour 1942
(Ehrennadel des Deutschen Jugendmeisters)

(a)	"Jugendmeister" Badge in Gold	$2,000
(b)	"Kampfspiele" Badge in Silver	1,000
(c)	"Kampfspiele" Badge in Bronze	1,000

Nr. 248

Dr. Klietmann

249. National Champions Badge of Honour 1942
(Ehrennadel des Reichssieger)

(a)	1st Class in Gold	$1,500
(b)	2nd Class in Silver	1,000
(c)	3rd Class in Bronze	800

Nr. 249

E. Zemaitis

Dr. Klietmann

250. Hitler Youth Proficiency Badge 1934
(Leistungsabzeichen der Hitler Jugend)

(a)	Grade I in Silver, in alloy or zinc	$40
(b)	Grade II in Bronze	50
(c)	Grade III in Black	60

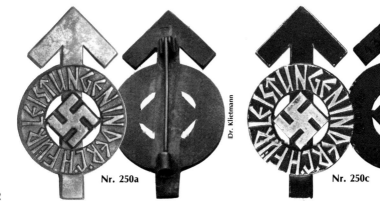

Dr. Klietmann

A. Forman

Nr. 250a

Nr. 250c

251. Hitler Youth Expert Skier Badge c. 1934
(H.J.Skiführerabzeichen)

(a)   Oxidised silver-plate and enamel. Double pin fitting $3,500

Nr. 251

Dr. Klietmann

John Coy

252. German Young Peoples Shooting Award
(Schiessauszeichnung des Deutschen Jungvolk)

(a)   D.J. Shooting Badge $50

Nr. 252

E. Zemaitis

253. Hitler Youth Shooting Awards
(H.J. Schiessauszeichnungen)

(a)   Badge for Good Shots $75
(b)   Badge for Marksmanship (Silver)   125
(c)   Badge for Champion Shots (Gold)   350

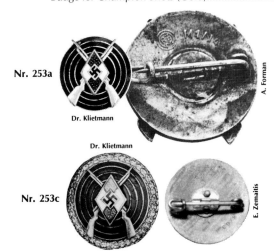

Nr. 253a

Dr. Klietmann

A. Forman

Dr. Klietmann

Nr. 253c

E. Zemaitis

254. German Young Peoples Proficiency Badge
   (Leistungsabzeichen des Deutschen Jungvolks)

(a) Silver grade badge in alloy or zinc $40

(b) Iron grade badge-blackened alloy or zinc 50

Nr. 254

255. League of German Girls Proficiency Clasp
   (B.D.M. Leistungsabzeichen)

(a) Silver grade clasp $300

(b) Bronze grade clasp 200

E. Zemaitis

Nr. 255

Dr. Klietmann

256. Young Girls Proficiency Clasp
   (Jungmadel Leistungsabzeichen)

(a) Silver clasp $250

E. Zemaitis

Dr. Klietmann

Nr. 256

257. Victors Badge in the National Trade Competition (H.J.) 1938
   (Siegerabzeichen im Reichsberufswettkampf)

(a) Type A   1st Pattern Award Badge 1937-H.J.
            Diamond within Cog emblem .... *

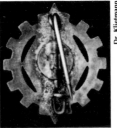

Nr. 257a, Type A

(b) Type B   2nd Pattern in plated metal
(c)   Kreissieger Badge with dates, "1938", "1939", "1944" $200
(d)   Gausieger Badge with dates, "1938", "1939", "1944"   400
(e)   Reichsieger Badge with dates, "1938", "1939", "1944"   1,000
(f)   Deluxe black case..   250

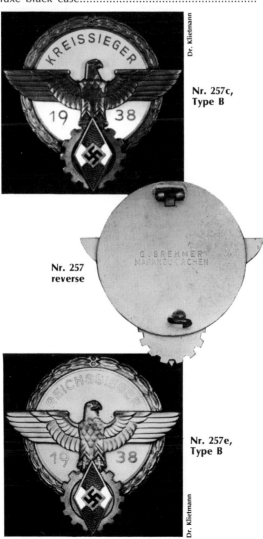

Nr. 257c,
Type B

Nr. 257
reverse

Nr. 257e,
Type B

Nr. 257f

Nr. 257d, painted
not enamel center

258. Decoration of the National Socialist German Students Federation (Ehrenzeichen des N.S.D. Studentenbundes)

(a)   Decoration $250

Nr. 258a

259. Golden Hitler Youth Badge of Honour with Oakleaves 1935 (Goldenes H.J. Ehrenzeichen mit Eichenlaub)

(a)   Early awards in hallmarked gold and enamel later
awards of fine quality, hallmarked silver-gilt
and enamel (Approx. 250 awarded).....................$1,000-2,000

260. Golden Hitler Youth Badge of Honour 1934 (Goldenes H.J. Ehrenabzeichen)

(a)   Badge... $175

Nr. 259a

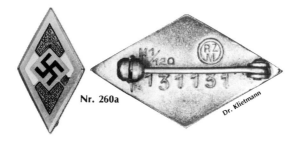

Nr. 260a

261. **Decoration of the High Command of the Hitler Youth for Distinguished Foreigners 1941**
(Ehrenzeichen der Reichsjugendführung der H.J. für Verdiente Ausländer)

(a)   Decoration $750

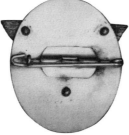

Nr. 261a

262 Medallion "For the Furthering of the Hitler Youth Hostel Building Program" 1937
(Plakette "Für die Förderung der Heimbeschaffung der H.J.")

(a)   Medallion $400

Nr. 262a

263. Civil Pilots Badge c. 1936
(Civil Flugzeugführer)

(a)   Deluxe quality silver & blue enamel badge,
           by "C.E. Juncker" of Berlin $850
(b)   Titled deluxe blue case 350

Dr. Klietmann

Nr. 263a

George Petersen

Civil-Flugzeugführer

Nr. 263b

264. Civil Radio Operators Badge
(Civil Bordfunker)

(a)	Fine quality silver badge, with maker's mark....................	$500
(b)	Titled deluxe blue case...	250

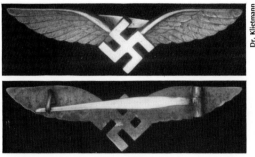

Nr. 264a

Nr. 264b

265. Civil Gliding Proficiency Badge
(Segelflieger-Abzeichen)

Badges in either bullion patches or enamel lapel badges. Also special
"Brilliants" award

(a)	"A" Certificate (one gull) Badge...	$40-60
(b)	"B" Certificate (two gulls) Badge.......................................	50-75
(c)	"C" Certificate (three gulls) Badge....................................	75-100

Nr. 265a   Nr. 265b   Nr. 265c

| (d) | Achievement "C" Certificate Badge (three gulls within oakleaf wreath)..................................... | 200 |
| (e) | Special Grade, "Brilliants" award. Inset with diamonds.. | * |

Nr. 265c

Nr. 265d

266. German Female Railway Staff Service Badge 1944 (Dienstnadel für Eisenbahnerinnen)

(a)	Gold Class (Not awarded)...	*
(b)	Silver Class..	$750
(c)	Bronze Class...	550

Dr. Klietmann

Nr. 266

Index

Luftwaffe Qualifications Badges & War Badges

Luftwaffe Non-Portable Awards

Armed Forces Long Service Awards

Political & Civil Awards

German Eagle Order

The German Order

German National Prize for Art & Science

German Red Cross Decorations

German Social Welfare Decorations

German Olympic Games Decorations

Civil Defence Decorations 1938

Fire Brigade Decorations 1936

Author's Request For Further Information and Illustrations

I am presently working on several book projects which include a companion volume on Third Reich Award Documents (military, political and civil) and values, as well as collating facts and gathering better illustrations for future editions of the ongoing Forman's Guide series. Therefore, I am interested in any photographs or photocopies of rare award documents, presentation folders or the many variations of award certificates for the more common decorations, awards, medals and combat badges. I also require illustrations of rare or interesting award presentation cases, cartons, titled paper packets or manufacturer's titled outer protective cardboard cartons for award cases. Photographs of the rare or interesting awards themselves, including the reverses are needed, plus again, any variations of manufacture or close-ups of maker's marks and hallmarks.

If you, the reader have anything you feel will be of interest to me, and ultimately, to the readership of future publications, please contact me. Remember, any book on this subject is an accumulation of facts and illustrations collated by an author, who has been aided by existing references and the unselfish generosity of others. This combined "team work" will result in a worthwhile addition to your book shelf.

Adrian Forman
608, Duncan House,
Dolphin Square,
London SW1, England

The author, Adrian Forman, has dealt with and collected medals for over twenty years. As an internationally recognized expert on this subject, he has been consulted by both Sotheby's and Christie's of London for his opinions on orders and medals. He has also contributed, for some years, to several of R. James Bender Publishing's (USA) specialized books on 3rd Reich subjects.

Errata

(1st Edition - Forman's Guide)

Text Nr.

24b	German Cross in Silver, Cloth Type B is in fact unofficial.
35	War Commemorative Medal 1939-1940. In fact, struck in Bronze for Combatants and in iron for non-combatants.
36	War Commemorative Medal 1939-1941. In fact, struck in Bronze for Combatants and in iron for non-combatants.
41	Omitted the later '1944' Bronze Award Bar. Doubtful if manufactured.
42	Photo of post 1945 Type without Swastika or Fascist emblems.
46	Error, should have read, 2nd Class in Bronze and not the nonexistent 3rd class.
60a	In fact, the only official Commemorative Cuff Title. Those of the Luftwaffe or Navy in blue or black with "Afrika" were worn by members of units in Africa, being the equivalent to the Africakorps cuff title.
72e	Only referred to standard badge and not the Deluxe Presentation Awards from Adolf Hitler. This was omitted in error.
74e	Only referred to standard Badges and not the (4) Deluxe Presentation awards from Reichsführer-SS Himmler in February 1945. This was omitted in error.
76	It is doubtful if the Silver Class was awarded at all.
77	Should have read as Black Grade I and not Silver Grade I as printed.
78	Should have read as Black Grade I and not Silver Grade I as printed.
78	Photograph of a post 1945 Type.
83	Should have listed all (3) classes; Gold, Silver and Black.
83c	Photograph of variant badge which should not have been used to illustrate the Type B maker marked , "2" on reverse. ("C.E. Juncker") .
86	Error, Type B dress copy did not exist as such although there are badges in Gilt-Tombak as well as Silver-Gilt by "Schwerin" of Berlin.
92	Error, Type B dress copy did not exist as such, although there are badges in Gilt-Tombak as well as Silver-Gilt.
92	Photograph of a unique variant in Gilt-Tombak, with 'Brilliants" and with reverse engraved with facsimile signature of 'Adolf Hilter'. (Ex Dr. K G. Klietmann).
94	Error, Type B dress copy did not exist as such, although badges exist with both Imitation Brilliants and low value diamonds, in hallmarked Silver-Gilt.
96	Error Type B dress copy did not exist as such.
99	A better translation of 'Frontspange' would be 'Combat Clasp', the word close should not have been included.
100	The basic qualification "swordfish" badge (Bewährungsabzeichen) , was omitted in error.
100	The grades were shown by error in reverse order, e.g., 100 (a) 1st Class was was in fact the 7th Class. All the Grades were printed in completely the reverse order.
102	Should have read Luftwaffe 1st Pattern Pilot Observers badge and not "Luftwaffe Aircrew Badge". This error was corrected in an article by Herr Patzwall, printed in Germany.
108	Omitted in error, the Luftwaffe Unqualified Air-Gunners badge 1944. Black wreath, silver eagle.
113b	Photograph is in the opinion of the author of a Post-1945 badge.
114a	Photograph is in the opinion of the author of a Post-1945 badge.

114c	Photograph is in the opinion of the author of a Post-1945 badge.
115	Photograph is in the opinion of the author of a Post-1945 badge.
126d	Photograph is, in fact, of the large blue leatherette box-case and not the rare deluxe 1st Type presentation red leather case which was shaped like a goblet.
131-136	Note: Over "20" different Luftwaffe plaques and shields have been mentioned in books including several variations of the more common types, plus several as yet not recorded in reference works on the subject.
138	Photograph for numbers 138a, 146a, 147a and 148a illustrates a variant breast star with short alternate radiants, rather than the standard issue breast star.
138	Omitted from text and illustrations is the extremely rare 1st pattern Eagle-Orders without the, 'fan' suspender. This 1st Pattern existed for only a few months and therefore, any class of this type would be worth 50% more than any equivalent Grade of Eagle Order in this catalogue.
153	Since the 1st edition, historical information was included in an Article by Herr. J. Nimmergut, (Germany-Infor Nr. 59. 1988) on the "10" Presentation awards of this order and the Rarity of the 1st Class and to a lesser degree, the 2nd and 3rd classes. Therefore the complete re-evaluation of the various classes in relation to Actual Presentation Awards, etc., has been complete in this new 2nd edition.
170	As several examples of this Medallion have been for sale (both named and unnamed specimens) , it has been re-evaluated in the 2nd edition.
173	Since 1st edition, historical information regarding only, "18" presentation awards (With Presentation Cased Miniature Award and Folder/Document) and the existence to date of only one documented piece on the collectors market. This, one of the Third Reichs most important Wartime awards, has been drastically re-evaluated, both historically and commercially, in the 2nd edition.
174	See 2nd edition text for complete re-evaluation of these awards, due to the small handful of presentation Gold Prize etc in late 1944 and early 1945, and accompanying national cash prize awards. 2nd only to the national prize for arts and science. This new grading makes the Fritz Todt prize and the Pioneer of Labour the Third Reich's highest awards for total war efforts of German industry and German workers, industrialists, engineers, scientists etc.
181	This badge should not have been included as it was merely a Police guard identity breast badge, bearing his official serial number.
188	Error, photograph of Blood Order number 3077 (2nd striking) is doubtful and should not have been used.
198	This badge exists in a quality bronze numbered issue.
202	Error, in fact the Gilt Class should read Gold Class.
205	Error, the official badge was in silver, while the bronze badge was the very common Rally Badge.
208	Omitted, the rare 1st Award dated, "1918" in error.
209e	Error, this is not an Award but merely a Collar device.
216	Photograph of a Post-1945 badge.
236	Error, should read, "3rd Class in iron" and not, "3rd Class in Bronze".
239	Omitted, type without Swastika and the female issue brooch award.
250	Omitted, the rare 1st pattern pre-1938 badge.
250	Error, in fact awards were only for Dates, 1938, 1939, and 1944.
258	Omitted, the silver and enamel lapel badges in various classes and special, "brilliants" award.
206	Third Reich medal-related reference books. Number two should have included "Schwert und Spaten", which joined with "Uniformen-Markt" in 1943 and was then re-titled "Deutsche - Uniformen Zeitung" (1943-45).
NOTE:	The above book list was intended as a brief guide to the English language readership on books related to the subject. Thus, several German text

reference books which German readers consider as "classic" references on the history of German awards and regulations were omitted. On reflection, it should have read, "Sample Book List Selection".

Bibliography

Angolia, LTC John R. For Führer & Fatherland, Military Awards of the Third Reich. San Jose, CA: R. James Bender Publishing Co., 1976.

Angolia, LTC John R. For Führer & Fatherland, Political and Civil Awards of the Third Reich. San Jose, CA: R. James Bender Publishing Co., 1978.

Archive Index Notes from Dr. K.G. Klietmann's Berlin Institute.

Doehle, Dr. Heinrich. Die Auszeichnungen des Grossdeutschen Reichs. 1940 & 1943 Editions.

Felligiebel, W.P. Die Träger des Ritterkreuzes des Eisernen Kreuzes 1939-45. 1986.

Hormann, J.N. "Altes Thema Und Seine Neuigkeiten (Nahkampfspange des Heeres in Gold.) German Info Journal Number 45. 1986.

Hormann, J.N. "Brillanten Von Heute Als Raritaten von Gestern". German Info Journal Number 59. 1988.

Hormann, J.N. "Eine Endgultige Geschichte" (Die Ehrentafelspange der Kriegsmarine. German Info Journal Number 53. 1987.

Hormann, J.N. Elite im Dritten Reich. (Deut.Akademie der Luftfahrtforschung 1936-1945). 1988.

Hormann, J.N. "Das Scharfschützen-Abzeichen Der Deutschen Wehrmacht". German Info Journal Number 54. 1987.

Hormann, J.N. "Der Nationalpreis für Kunst und Wissenschaft 1937". German Info Journal Number 50. 1987.

Klietmann, Dr. K.G. Auszeichnungen des Deutschen Reiches 1936-1945. 1981.

Klietmann, Dr. K.G. Deutsche Auszeichnungen. 1971.

Klietmann, Dr. K.G. Deutsche Auszeichnungen. 1964.

Littlejohn, David and Dodkins, Col. C.M. Order, Decorations Medals and Badges of The Third Reich. San Jose, CA: R. James Bender Publishing Co., 1968.

Littlejohn, David and Dodkins, Col. C.M. Order, Decorations Medals and Badges of The Third Reich Volume II. 1973.

Littlejohn, David with Hinds, H. The Hitler Youth. 1988.

Nimmergut, J. "Der Deutsche Orden" German Info Journal Number 59. 1988.

Nimmergut, J. Das Eiserne Kreuz 1813-1939. (Deut.Ordensmuseum.) 1990.

Nimmergut, J. "Pionier der Arbeit". Orden-Militaria-Magazin Number 41. 1991.

Patzwall, K.D. "Das Gemeinsame Flugzeugführer-und Beobachterabzeichen 1.Model". Militaria Heft 2. 1988.

Patzwall, K.D. "Das Werftleitungsabzeichen" Militaria,Heft 5. 1990.

Reichsgesetzblatt, Jahrgang 1939, "Teil 1 - 1575-1576". (Courtesy of V.E. Bowen).

ADRIAN FORMAN

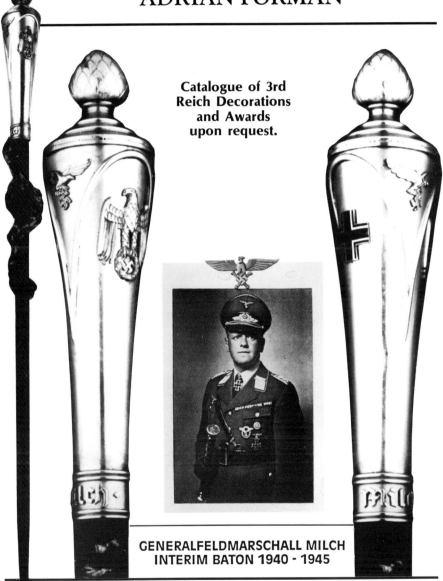

Catalogue of 3rd
Reich Decorations
and Awards
upon request.

**GENERALFELDMARSCHALL MILCH
INTERIM BATON 1940 - 1945**

A superb and unique historical piece . . . price upon request

A donation from the sale of this book
will be made by the author to:

Befrienders
International
Developing Volunteer Action To Prevent Suicide

Befrienders International
UK Reg. Charity Nr. 326693

"Befrienders International" was established in the UK in 1974. It represents 28 autonomous national organizations throughout the world, including the USA. Befrienders International works to support people in crisis and prevent suicide. For details of this work and service, contact Befrienders International, 228 Bishopsgate, London, England, EC2M 4QD. Registered as a Charity UK 326693.